The Guide
Cambridge University Botanic Garden

Contents

The daisy family, *Compositae*, on the Systematic Beds with globe thistles, *Echinops* species, to the fore

Welcome

The swamp cypress, *Taxodium distichum*, in autumn

Welcome to Cambridge University Botanic Garden, home to a living plant collection beautifully displayed in a seamless patchwork of gardens, and set within a wonderful collection of trees. Over 8000 plant species from around the world, including nine National Collections®, are cultivated across this 40 acre heritage-listed Garden, representing an unparalleled resource for teaching and research, and a place enjoyed by many.

This present Garden was opened in 1846, and was the vision of John Stevens Henslow, Professor of Botany from 1825-1861. The western half of the site was landscaped not only as a place of beauty, enjoyed by generations, but also as a botanic garden devoted to the study of plants in their own right, and to the understanding of their diversity and origins. The meandering paths take you past trees and herbs arranged to show their family relationships, illustrating ideas about variation and the nature of species. This would ultimately be taken up in a revolutionary fashion by Henslow's most famous student, Charles Darwin.

Henslow also persuaded the University to establish a major tree collection inspired by the many exotic introductions arriving into the country in the 19th century and we enjoy this legacy today. The backdrop of mature trees, the best collection in the eastern region, now also includes several champion specimens and the first trees to be planted in the UK of the dawn redwood, *Metasequoia glyptostroboides*, and the giant redwood, *Sequoiadendron giganteum*.

In the 1950s, the Garden was extended to occupy the eastern half of the site, and themed to demonstrate horticultural principles and grouping of plants.

Our mission is both to maintain the living plant collections of the University for today and the future, and to provide public access to them. The study of plants and education remains at the heart of the Garden, which continues to be an inspiration for all – researchers, gardeners or school children – and the landscape is a refreshing oasis for all our visitors. We hope today that we continue to plant ideas, maybe even seeds of change, as we work to reflect and communicate new directions in plant science, respond to the challenges of managing an historic landscape and deliver innovative outreach and education programmes for all.

Designed for both year-round interest and seasonal inspiration, you will find plants to intrigue and enchant whenever you visit. Enjoy.

What we do

Lavandula angustifolia 'Hidcote'. The genus Lavandula is a major research collection

Accession Number — 20030266 A   APONOGETONACEAE — Family

Scientific name —
Aponogeton distachyus

Common name —
Water hawthorn

Distribution — Temp S Africa   G — Provenance

Research

Since its foundation, the Botanic Garden has been a focus and stimulus for science in the University. For example, at the end of the 19th century, William Bateson of Trinity College grew a range of plants on Garden plots to help understand heredity, coining the word 'genetics' for this new science.

The research collections of plants, the Cory Library of horticultural and taxonomic books, the Garden's own Herbarium, our facilities and horticultural expertise are all provided for any member of the University of Cambridge to use in their scholarship. Recently, research projects have been carried out by staff and students of Archaeology, Engineering, Genetics, Geography, Geology, Plant Sciences and Zoology. Studies on plants cover a wide spectrum of activities – biophysics, ecology, genetics, molecular biology and physiology. The landscape of the Garden provides an important resource for students of architecture, while the animal life of the Garden can be readily studied in this protected and diverse environment. The Garden is, essentially, an outdoor laboratory.

Many of the Garden's plant collections, including those held under the Plant Heritage National Plant Collection® scheme, have arisen out of research by Garden staff and have resulted in several major monographs. These include publications on lady's mantle, *Alchemilla*, by previous Garden Director, Dr Max Walters, on hardy geranium by former garden taxonomist, Dr Peter Yeo, and more recently on lavender, *Lavandula*, by Garden Curator, Dr Tim Upson. Conservation work has focused on the endangered plants of East Anglia with current projects underway on the Fen ragwort, *Senecio paludosus*, the Fen orchid, *Liparis loeslii*, and the Fen violet, *Viola persicifolia*.

We welcome opportunities to collaborate with botanic gardens worldwide and other partner organisations in conservation, as well as with researchers from other universities, horticultural colleges and further education colleges.

Plant Labels

Plant labels provide the key information on the identity of the specimen and are vital to the research value of the collection. The unique accession number in the top left corner of each plant label links the specimen growing in the Garden to the information about that particular plant stored on the Garden's database. The first four digits of the number show the year the plant was accessioned into the collection. The last four digits are given sequentially to each plant or seed packet as it comes into the collection during the calendar year. Sometimes we don't know the date when a plant came into the collection, particularly for historical specimens, and thus their accession numbers begin with 1000.

The plant family is shown at the top right of the label and the plant's scientific name appears across the centre of the label with the common English name, if there is one, underneath. The natural distribution range of the plant is shown at the bottom left. In the bottom right corner of the label is a single letter. This is the provenance or source code. 'G' indicates the plant is of garden origin; 'W' indicates the plant was collected directly from the wild; 'Z' indicates the plant is from a cultivated plant descended from one of known wild origin.

Ensuring that all the plants in the collections are labelled is a major and continuous undertaking. Labels have always suffered damage, and even theft! An article in Loudon's *Magazine of Natural History* from 1833 describes the habit of jackdaws stealing labels from the original City-centre Botanic Garden to make their nests: 'from the chimney shaft, Dr Kerrick's man-servant got out on one occasion eighteen dozen labels'.

Occasionally plant names change as scientific research sheds new light on relationships. In recent years, this has been particularly significant at the family level. Currently we are continuing to use the traditional and still well recognised family names. We plan to change these in due course although it will be an extensive job. So, for example, you will still find our lime trees, *Tilia*, labelled in the family *Tiliaceae*, although the most modern treatments now place them in the mallow family, *Malvaceae*.

Horticulture

This Grade II* listed heritage Garden opened on this site in 1846 and has been cared for by generations of horticulturists. Their expert skill, vision and dedication are reflected in the quality of the design and high standards of maintenance.

A dedicated team of 21 horticulturists care for the Garden, organised under seven sections: Alpine & Woodland; Demonstration & Display; Experimental; Glasshouse; Landscape & Machinery; Systematics; and, Trees & Shrubs.

We are also committed to training and supporting the next generation of professional horticulturists. Each year we offer six horticultural trainee places on the Cambridge Certificate in Practical Horticulture and Plantsmanship.

Gardening in Cambridge

With an average annual rainfall of just 557 mm of rain, Cambridge is in the driest region of Britain. Cambridge also has a more continental climate than most of Britain,

The reserve alpine collection

Formal lawns set off the architecture of the Garden

...ing up a new display

with particularly warm summer temperatures; the warmest month is usually July with an average of 22°C, and with an all time high of 38°C.

The soils of the Botanic Garden are silts and sands derived from the flood plain of the River Cam nearby. These soils, slightly alkaline in pH, are about one metre in depth and overlie a layer of chalk and flints, with gault clay deep down. This soil is stony, light and relatively free draining, and is easily worked even after rain.

We have been recording weather data at the Botanic Garden since 1904 and supply daily figures to the Meteorological Office at Bracknell. The monthly rainfall records are published on the Garden's website. Analysis of the records show that over the last 100 years our average temperature has risen by 1.2°C and the hottest day, highest monthly and yearly average have all occurred within the last 10 years. Rainfall has been less predictable with no clear pattern.

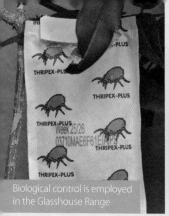
Biological control is employed in the Glasshouse Range

Turning the compost heaps

We grow thousands of plants from se each year for the Systematic Beds

A sustainable approach

The Botanic Garden aims to practice sustainable horticulture. In all our operations, we try to reduce the materials we use, limit chemical and high energy inputs and recycle as much as possible. We approach this in a holistic way, so by encouraging wildlife we have our natural pest control, by recycling our green waste we can mulch beds and avoid the need to water.

Water is a precious resource locally. We limit watering to any new plantings of annuals, herbs and trees while they establish. Occasionally, during prolonged dry periods, we may water some of the ornamental lawns to improve their ability to tolerate visitor pressure and large events. We also select plants that are well-suited to our dry climate and do not require extra watering to grow. However, at the end of a dry summer some plants may look limp and drop their leaves early. This is a natural response to dry conditions and the plants suffer no long-term harm.

The Garden has an army of birds, insects and amphibians to control pests and diseases. By encouraging a diverse range of wildlife over many decades, we have achieved a balance between pests and predators. Outdoors, we accept a low level of pests and hence some damage to plants but this means we rarely need to use chemicals. In the sheltered environment of the Glasshouse Range, however, pests can quickly become a problem, and here we employ an integrated pest management plan. This primarily uses biological control, whereby a range of predators are introduced through the season to control pests. In 1964, a tiny wasp, *Encarsia formosa*, was collected in the

Garden's Glasshouse Range which has proved a highly effective parasite of white fly. You will see little packets containing the eggs of this tiny wasp attached to plants throughout the Glasshouse Range.

The Garden produces a vast amount of green and wood waste every year, which we recycle and reuse on site, creating a sustainable closed loop. The raw material is stockpiled until there is sufficient to shred the waste into small particles ready for composting. Through the action of bacteria, the shredded waste starts to breakdown heating up in the process. The compost heap starts to steam, and can reach 60-70°C, sufficient heat to kill weed seeds and pests. Once matured, it is spread onto beds and around plants as a mulch. This improves soil structure and helps retain moisture, encouraging healthy plant growth.

Most wood is processed into woodchips which are used to mulch beds and top-dress informal paths. Some pieces of wood may be used for sculpture, timber or processed as firewood, ensuring nothing is wasted from site.

Wildlife

We actively encourage a great diversity of wildlife in the Garden as part of our sustainable approach to horticulture. This makes the Garden a green oasis in the City and we are recognised as a city wildlife site particularly for the invertebrates and mosses that occur here.

Birds are numerous in the Botanic Garden, which offers abundant food supply and safe nesting sites. Over 100 species have been recorded with the most easily seen being blackbirds, robins and the ubiquitous wood pigeon. The Lake is home to moorhens and mallards which usually raise several broods of ducklings each year. A pair of sparrowhawks often nest and can be heard calling as they fly over the Garden in summer.

There are good populations of grass snakes, which are most often seen around the Lake, in the Fen Display, or sometimes basking on the Rock Garden. Frogs and toads are both present and their spawn is a common sight in the slow-flowing stream in the spring breeding season. The Fen Display is a good place to spot smooth newts, which otherwise seek the moist shelter beneath rotting logs.

The invertebrate life of the Garden is very diverse and includes many species of butterflies and moths, flies, aphids, spiders, dragonflies, bees and wasps. The flowers in the Bee Borders, Scented Garden and Systematic Beds are particularly good places to spot a wide range of nectar-feeding insects.

The most obvious wild mammals in the Garden are the grey squirrels, which are relatively tame and active during the day. Occasionally, visitors may spot a chestnut brown muntjac deer, about the size of a large dog. Most mammals, however, including foxes and badgers, are active from dusk to dawn.

A common frog, *Rana temporaria*

The Garden supports a good population of grass snakes, *Natrix natrix*

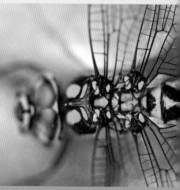

A southern hawker dragonfly, *Aeshna cyanea*

Education & Outreach

The Garden is an inspirational, natural outdoor classroom for all ages; a place to develop knowledge, encourage creativity and bring learning to life. Education has been central to the Garden's mission since its foundation, historically focused on the teaching of University students, but today we help fulfil the University's commitment to widening participation with programmes for all.

We welcome visits to the Garden from schools and colleges in all seasons and offer imaginative learning opportunities across the curriculum and key stages. Science and Plants for Schools (SAPS), based in the Garden, is a UK-wide programme dedicated to stimulating plant science in the classroom by providing science teachers with practical and inspirational teaching resources.

The Garden offers a lively programme of formal courses, talks and events. These cover horticulture, plant identification, botanical illustration and creative workshops. For families, there's a great choice of activities through the year that encourage exploration of the natural world.

We are greatly supported in all we do by a growing corps of volunteers.

COTONEASTER Cratæ

VIBURNUM

Sprig of Judas

Jasmine

DER

Cypress

THE SOIL
of the garden
is gravelly
and porous

OAK

Monkey
Puzzle

Birch

Acer Davidii

The gardens are
open to the public
all the week
except Sunday

Wellingtonia Deodar pinus

Juniper

RCH on the East side of the garden

DON
PLANE

US BEECH

Allotments occupy about 18 acres

HAZEL

Larix Larch

THE LAWN

Cedar

THE
PRUNUS
PLOT

LEBAN

Prunus

Cherry

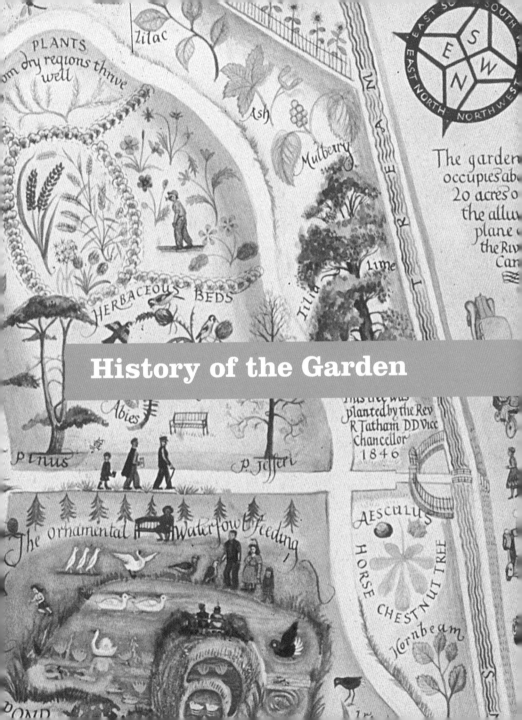

History of the Garden

The original Botanic Garden

The original Botanic Garden of Cambridge University was founded in 1762 in the City centre on what is now known as the New Museums Site. This typical physic garden of just five acres, donated to the University by Richard Walker, Vice Master of Trinity College, expressly for the purpose, was principally dedicated to the cultivation of herbaceous plants used in the teaching of medical students. A small commemorative plot along Free School Lane, adjacent to the original site, is maintained with some of the plants originally grown in this garden.

Henslow's 19th century Garden

John Stevens Henslow, painted c1840-50, British School

We owe the existence of the present much larger Botanic Garden, sandwiched between Hills Road and Trumpington Road, to John Stevens Henslow, Professor of Botany at Cambridge from 1825-1861. With his energy and political skill, Henslow persuaded the University that if serious experimental botany was to take its rightful place in the upsurge of natural science studies at Cambridge, the Botanic Garden needed to move to a larger site, and that this new Garden should be for the study of the plants themselves.

A green field 16-hectare (40 acre) site one mile south of the city centre was acquired from Trinity Hall by the University in 1831, but legal wrangles prevented immediate development. Planting finally began in 1846, but the University only sanctioned the development of the western half on grounds of expense. Plans were drawn up by the first Garden Curator, Andrew Murray, consisting of a sinuous path following the circumference of the western Garden, bisected by the Main Walk. A belt of trees, grouped together in their families was planted outside the perimeter path. The U-shaped Lake and a complex series of herbaceous Systematic

Staff photo with Curator, William Mudd, centre in the top hat, 1866

Perambulators were only allowed into the Garden from 1969

Beds are original features. The design represents the 'gardenesque' style of the time, combining both specimen plants and composed landscapes.

There are a few later additions to this landscape: the Glasshouse Range along the northern boundary; a splendid fountain, which provides the eastern focal point to the Main Walk; and, the Limestone Rock Garden, designed and built adjacent to the lake in the 1950s. The beautiful wrought iron gates of the original City-centre Botanic Garden were moved to head the Trumpington Road end of the Main Walk in 1909.

The Garden since 1951

The eastern part of the original land purchase remained undeveloped until the University was able to apply a magnificent legacy from Reginald Cory, received in 1934. Cory had been a life-long benefactor of the Garden since his undergraduate days at Trinity College, and his legacy unlocked the remaining 20 acres of land for development by the Garden. This exciting task fell to John Gilmour, Director, and Bob Younger, Superintendent of the Garden. Work began in 1951.

Although the western and eastern parts are stylistically linked through a consistently 'gardenesque' style and the continuation of the sinuous perimeter path, they are very

The Sainsbury Laboratory Cambridge University was opened by the Queen in 2011

different in feel, character and curatorial content. This disjunct reflects how plant science studies have changed in focus since the Garden's foundation in the mid 19th century.

Whereas Murray's 19th century plan for the western 20 acres focused on the naming and organising of individual species into family groupings, the eastern part of the Garden is generally concerned with how plant communities develop. Thus, the 20th century science of ecology permeates the philosophy of the British Wild Plants collections, horticultural principles are demonstrated in the Scented and Winter Gardens, and climate and sustainability issues dominate the thematic plantings of the Dry Garden.

Into the 21st century

During the first decade of this century, major developments have been focused on the development of a new research institute for the University devoted to understanding plant development. The Sainsbury Laboratory Cambridge University was opened in 2011 representing a major international investment in plant sciences. This Laboratory, hosted within the Garden, is a private facility, but visitors can enjoy the architecture of the award-winning building from the Garden Café.

In order to accommodate the Laboratory, new infrastructure was built behind-the-scenes including new experimental glasshouses, a new machinery barn and workshops, as well as the re-housing of the reserve Glasshouse collections in new purpose-built glasshouses. A new visitor entrance and associated landscaping opened at Brookside in 2008, where the Garden's main offices are also accommodated.

Gardens are dynamic by their nature. The development plan for the Garden seeks to respect the heritage areas while reflecting the importance of plants in addressing major global issues. Climate change is expected to influence this Garden greatly in the future and is already being taken into account with new plantings.

Iris sibirica 'Caesar's Brother' in the Cory Lawn plantings

Plantings & Gardens

Early summer in the Stream Garden, with pale lilac spires of *Veronicastrum virginicum*

Stream Garden

The western boundary of the Botanic Garden is formed by Hobson's Conduit, a canalised water course dating from 1610 that brings clean water in to Cambridge from springs at the base of the Gog Magog hills four miles to the south. A channel running between the thicket of Caucasian wingnut, *Pterocarya fraxinifolia*, diverts some of this clear chalky water into the Botanic Garden to form a stream that replenishes the Lake.

A flowing stream is a rare sight in eastern England and presents an opportunity to grow a great variety of bog and water-loving species. In early spring, yellow flowers dominate, with rafts of native kingcup, *Caltha palustris*, appearing to float mid-stream, and stands of the American skunk cabbage, *Lysichiton americanus*, lining the banks with its remarkable flowers consisting of a waxy yellow sheath wrapped around a central, columnar spadix.

Later, elegant stands of Sibirian iris, *Iris sibirica* 'Perry's Blue', create a strong upright dynamic against the enormous puckered leaves of the ornamental rhubarb, *Rheum palmatum*. Exotic primroses, *Primula*, feathery *Astilbe* and clouds of mauve flowers of meadow rues, *Thalictrum*, transform the scene. Loosestrifes, *Lythrum*, both native and cultivar, provide late vivid magenta colour. The interest is continued with later-flowering *Rodgersia* and *Ligularia*. There is a bed near the Lake of magnificent, barely-contained great horsetail, *Equisetum telmateia*, stretching up to one metre high.

Among the horsetails are masses of a parasitic plant, the purple toothwort, *Lathraea clandestina*. Throughout April it has brilliant purple hooded flowers at ground level which are scattered along the stream and the borders of the Lake. It has no chlorophyll and hence is unable to synthesise its own food, obtaining its nutrients instead from the roots of willows and poplars.

Lilium columbianum

Woodland Garden

Between the Stream Garden and the Lake, a dense Woodland Garden has been developed to display unusual trees and woodland understorey plants from around the world, which can be explored via a lattice of meandering bark-chipped paths.

In deepest winter, wintersweets, *Chimonanthus praecox*, saturate the air with their alluring and spicy scent. In spring, before the leaf canopy develops, the rich tapestry of understorey plants begins to emerge. The leaves of the ostrich fern, *Matteuccia struthiopteris*, unfurl and stretch into large shuttlecocks above a carpet of *Anemone*, *Epimedium* and *Scilla*. Later, boldly foliaged *Rodgersia* species with creamy flowers are striking. Thanks to a generous 'In Memory' gift, the understorey plants have recently been greatly bolstered with the emphasis on Northern hemisphere woodland plants. The central beds are now geographically planted to represent the woodland communities of North America, Asia and Europe. Some pan-Northern hemisphere genera, like the bugbanes, *Actaea,* including *Cimicifuga*, have different species planted for comparison in the various continental beds.

On the northern edge of the Woodland Garden during May, the branches of the handkerchief or dove tree, *Davidia involucrata,* are hung with fluttering pairs of unequal bright-white bracts. Deeper within the Woodland Garden, by the Lake edge, is an example of the foxglove tree, *Paulownia tomentosa*. Also by the Lake edge is a fine golden rain tree, *Koelreuteria paniculata*, which, in summer, produces enormously long and airy panicles of lemon-yellow, irregular, star-shaped flowers, followed in autumn by inflated 3-seamed papery seedpods. The late-flowering bottlebrush buckeye, *Aesculus parviflora*, is conspicuous in July when it is smothered in a profusion of erect white inflorescences or 'candles', each with striking bright red anthers. The foliage of this species is currently unaffected by the horse chestnut leaf miner moth, responsible for bringing an early autumn to a great majority of the UK common horse chestnuts, *Aesculus hippocastanum*, by turning the leaves prematurely brown. Katsura trees,

Cercidiphyllum japonicum, provide spring and, in particular, autumn interest when the delightful paired heart shaped leaves turn shades of rich apricot and smoky pink, and emit an enticing caramel fragrance.

Between the Woodland Garden and the Stream Garden are some superb groups of bamboo. They were initially established in 1884 by the Garden's Curator, Richard Lynch, who claimed it was 'the first ornamental Bamboo collection' in the UK. The decorative screening qualities of *Phyllostachys* make the entrance to the Bog Garden irresistibly secretive.

Although woodland plants often come from areas of higher rainfall, we strive to grow them without irrigation.

A toad lily, *Tricyrtis stolonifera*

Admiring *Cornus* 'Norman Hadden'

Late spring in the Woodland Garden

The fiddlecocks of ostrich fern, *Matteucia struthiopteris*, unfurl in late spring.

Late spring in the Bog Garden

Bog Garden

As the stream enters the Lake, some of the water is channeled off to form a Bog Garden around a shallow inlet, a secret and enclosed space entered by pushing through dense clumps of bamboo and crossing a small bridge where a beautiful swamp cypress, *Taxodium distichum*, rises from the water. This deciduous conifer turns to a coppery ember in the autumn.

Protected by steeply shelving terraced banks on three sides, the Bog Garden provides a sheltered and shady microclimate that encourages spring flowers such as exotic primroses, *Primula*, to thrive, alongside marsh-loving sedges, grasses and the airy sprays of salad burnet, *Sanguisorba*, and the ornamental thistle, *Cirsium rivulare*.

Amongst the many ferns, the rare native royal fern, *Osmunda regalis,* forms an imposing clump, and is at least 60 years old. This plant has suffered from extensive collection from the wild and is now extinct in many parts of the country. Here also, an unusual shrub, *Itea ilicifolia*, makes a great late summer show when the handsome holly-like leaves contrast with the long, drooping racemes of greenish-white flowers.

Picking runner beans in the Schools' Garden

Schools' Garden

The Schools' Garden is where school groups get involved with practical horticulture, growing and caring for vegetables, fruits, flowers and herbs. Here, young gardeners can experience the magic of sowing seeds, taking cuttings and propagating plants, right through to harvesting. Most of all, this is where children can enjoy working outdoors. The design for the Schools' Garden was inspired by the creative and sometimes radical design ideas of children at our partner schools in the project.

We are grateful to the very many supporters who have helped us make the Schools' Garden possible, through financial contributions and a lot of hard volunteer graft. Please note that the Schools' Garden may be closed to visitors when a school is in there working.

Dianthus carthusianorum on the Limestone Rock Garden

Rock Gardens

The Limestone Rock Garden surrounds the north-eastern arm of the Lake. Construction of the Rock Garden took four years (1954-58) with each rock, some weighing up to three tonnes, winched into place with a tripod and block-lifting system. The horticultural staff then levelled and positioned the stones using crowbars to create a range of planting niches – angles that shade, nooks that shelter, and crevices that collect water – in which to grow plants from rocky regions around the world.

These specialised rock plants are laid out geographically. On the south side of the Lake, among the detached rocks, are plants of South African and Australasian origin. Proceeding anticlockwise are mountain plants from Asia, then Europe, including the European representatives of the Garden's National Collections of saxifrage, *Saxifraga*, and lady's mantle, *Alchemilla*. Finally, North American species occupy the highest point and its flanks, and include a prickly pear cactus, *Opuntia*, which survives and even flowers in this exposed habitat.

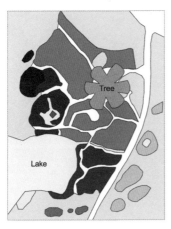

Rock garden plants are usually very colourful and are characterised by a high density of flowers on rather small plants. This reflects the low frequency of pollinators that occur in desolate, rocky and usually dry areas. The

Limestone Rock Garden has a long flowering season but is most spectacular in late spring and early summer. Mountain plants are also usually small ground-huggers, and can be easily damaged. Please take care to stay on the paths through the Rock Garden, which although narrow, uneven and occasionally slippery, are intrinsic to the original design and vision.

To the west of the Limestone Rock Garden is a small Sandstone Rock Garden that can be reached via the stepping stones across the Lake. Here, shade and moisture loving plants, including some lime-hating plants (calcifuges) are grown: members of the heather, *Ericaceae*, family survive, although the chalky ground water reduces their life expectancy. Bulbs such as *Trillium* and dog's tooth violet, *Erythronium dens-canis*, flower here beneath *Prunus serrulata* 'Alboplena', a neatly-shaped flowering cherry, which in May is thickly covered in brilliant white, double flowers.

The woolly foxglove, *Digitalis lanata*

Symphyandra armena

Primula sikkimensis

from the top of the Limestone Rock Garden

The Fountain that heads the Main Walk is a natural gathering spot

Main Walk

The Main Walk stretches east-west from the iconic Fountain, designed by cutler David Mellor and completed in 1970, to Trumpington Road, where the 18th century gates to the original Botanic Garden were moved in 1909. The wide gravel path is flanked by majestic, coniferous trees, some of which are amongst the most important trees in the Garden's collection.

Both ends of the Main Walk are marked by huge specimens of the giant redwood, *Sequoiadendron giganteum*. The two redwoods opposite one another near the Fountain are grown from the first seed brought back by William Lobb from California and were planted in 1855. Three young redwoods have been planted, two near the Fountain and one by the Trumpington Road Gates, to ensure continuity should the life of these giants prove to be (relatively) short in Cambridge.

The most important group of trees is the collection of subspecies of *Pinus nigra*, initially planted together by the Garden's founder, Professor John Henslow. This includes a pair of black pines planted opposite each other on the western section of the Main Walk. *Pinus nigra* subsp. *nigra* from Austria is a narrow upright tree with few, downward sloping branches that allow snowfall to slide off. The short stiff needles are held in dense bunches. The Pyrenean pine from Spain, *P. nigra* subsp. *salzmannii*, in contrast, is a spreading tree with an open canopy of long needles. These subspecies illustrate the extremes of variation within this species. The Main Walk has specimens of other pines such as the stone pine, *Pinus pinea*, big cone pine, *P. coulteri*, and the Bhutan pine, *P. wallichiana*, which will ensure that the stateliness and magnificence of the Main Walk will continue into the future.

A diverse group of cedars at the intersection of the Main Walk and Henslow Walk includes the Lebanon cedar, *Cedrus libani*, Atlas cedar, *C. atlantica*, from Morocco, and deodar cedar, *C. deodara*. Again, this grouping points to the profound influence that Henslow has had on the planting philosophy for the Botanic Garden.

The potato, *Solanaceae*, family plantings on the Systematic Beds, with petunias and tobacco plants to the fore

Systematic Beds

Systematic Beds (sometimes called 'Order Beds') are used for teaching plant taxonomy, the science of naming and classifying organisms. Related species of plants are grown together in family beds, allowing shared features and differences to be easily shown and compared, usually based on the structure of the flowers.

In most botanic gardens, beds are long and rectangular. In contrast, the Systematic Beds in Cambridge all differ in size and are set out as curving, irregular island beds. The visual effect in the height of summer is a great kaleidoscopic mosaic of flowering plants covering some three acres. No more than one family is placed in a bed, but large families such as the daisy family, *Compositae*, and the grasses, *Gramineae*, have many beds.

The Systematic Beds were designed by the first Curator of the Botanic Garden, Andrew Murray, who set out to translate into a planting design the most comprehensive book on plant classification of the time, written in 1819 by the Swiss botanist Augustin de Candolle. In his book, de Candolle distinguished between two major groups: plants with one seed leaf (monocotyledons) and those with two seed leaves (dicotyledons). Murray created a central oval enclosed by a low hawthorn hedge in which to gather the monocotyledon families, which account for about 20% of flowering plants. He then arranged the dicotyledon families in order around the oval beginning with page one of de Candolle's book, which concerned the buttercup family, *Ranunculaceae*, and ending, as de Candolle did, with the American pokeweed family, *Phytolaccaceae*.

The Systematic Beds hold a scientific collection of about 1600 species belonging to about 98 families in 157 beds. But they are more than this. The Systematic Beds represent an extensive living textbook that expresses in visual form de Candolle's philosophical ideas about the world of plants.

Aerial view over the Systematic Beds, which group plants together in families. The central oval displays the monocotyledon plants surrounded by four quadrants displaying the dicotyledon plants.

e plant portraits are selected to show the diversity of the potato family, *Solanaceae*. Clockwise from top: *Nicotiana rustica*, fruits
e Chinese lantern, *Physalis alkekengii*, the tobacco plant, *Nicotiana tabacum*, *Schizanthus pinnatus*, fruits of *Solanum sisymbrifolium*.

Silver leaves are a common characteristic of many Mediterranean plants

Mediterranean Beds

These beds house a representative selection of plants from around the Mediterranean Basin. They form part of a larger collection of plants from the five areas of the world that have a Mediterranean climate, that is, cool wet winters and hot dry summers. The close-by Continents Apart House and its surrounding outdoor bays show plants from the Mediterranean areas of South Africa and Australia. Adjacent bays include plants from California and Chile.

Plants from the Mediterranean Basin are by far the most important for UK gardeners and include popular shrubs such as rock roses, *Cistus*, and lavenders, *Lavandula*, while fastigiate pencil cedar, *Cupressus sempervirens*, and Spanish broom, *Spartium junceum*, a pea relative, provide feature plants. Bulbs and annuals, both important life forms in the Mediterranean, are well represented. This area extends to the entrance patio of the Glasshouse Range where the emphasis is on economic plants from the Mediterranean Basin and here fig, *Ficus carica*, pomegranate, *Punica granatum*, and bay laurel, *Laurus nobilis*, can be found.

As one of the driest parts of the UK, Cambridgeshire is well suited to the cultivation of Mediterranean plants.

The central Palm House is home to the Tropical Rainforests display

The Glasshouse Range

The Glasshouse Range flanks the north side of the Main Lawn, and is full of year-round interest, from the daintiest alpine to exotic tropical climbers. It is a real refuge on a cold day. The Range has been transformed in the last decade through a major restoration and replanting programme that has seen the glasshouse plants, all requiring some protection from the Cambridge climate, re-presented to reveal the drama of plant diversity and to explore how plants have evolved to survive in key environments such as icy mountains, oceanic islands, desert and tropical rainforests.

These environment-focused displays occupy a suite of houses connected by an ornamental corridor running the full 180 metre length of the Glasshouse Range, planted with tender, showy plants such as passionflowers, bougainvillea, hibiscus, orchids and bird-of-paradise plants.

As each house of the Glasshouse Range projects from the connecting spine, the external spaces inbetween enjoy a protected microclimate and are known as the Glasshouse Bays. The plantings here have been designed to extend the theme of the drama of diversity by taking the landscapes and collections within the houses out into the Bays to test their hardiness. Thus the Bay adjacent to the Arid Lands house is planted up with an architectural mix of cacti, *Echeveria*, *Agave* and other succulents to complement and extend the desert landscape within. Similarly, outside the Continents Apart display, you will find kangaroo paws, *Anigozanthos*, and bottlebrush, *Callistemon*, thriving alongside many colourful South African and Australian bulbous species including *Agapanthus*, *Crocosmia* and *Dianella*. Adjacent to the central Tropical Rainforests display, we are trialling papyrus, *Cyperus papyrus*, outside in submerged tanks alongside the pairing of castor oil plant, *Ricinus communis*, and giant montbretia, *Crocosmia masonorum*, to give a hot, tropical feeling.

The Glasshouse Range

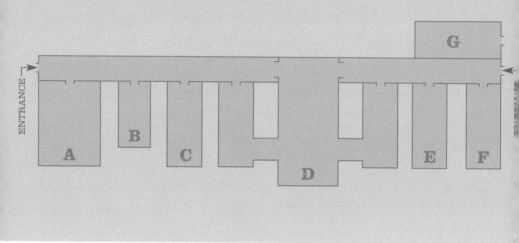

A Continents Apart: two continents, a shared origin

The Temperate House is home to Continents Apart, a display focusing on the floristically rich Cape region of South Africa and on south-west Australia. These areas are particularly rich with endemic plants – over three-quarters of species found here grow wild nowhere else on earth.

With so many exotic and unusual flowering plants, including the king protea, *Protea cynaroides*, and pincushion proteas, *Leucospermum*, from South Africa, and the grass trees, *Xanthorrhoea*, and aptly-named kangaroo paw, *Anigozanthos*, from Australia, the plantings provide a horticultural display to excite the eye.

When flowering plants first appeared, Australia and South Africa were joined as part of the supercontinent called Gondwana, which started to break up around 180 million years ago. Continents Apart explores how plant families that originated in Gondwana and are still common to Australia and South Africa today, like the *Proteaceae*, evolved into different but related groups once these land masses drifted apart. Both floras also exhibit a fascinating dependency on bushfire for regeneration.

Cotyledon tomentosum

Leucospermum cuneiforme

Anigozanthos flavidus

B Oceanic Islands: evolving in isolation

This display highlights the unique floras of oceanic islands, and the intense conservation challenges they typically face. The Canary Islands feature prominently, with ornamental species such as marguerite daisies, *Argyranthemum*, succulent *Aeonium* and drought-resistant lavenders. These plants illustrate the dramatic evolution of different forms on oceanic islands, a common phenomenon of these floras.

Aeonium lindleyi

Echium candicans

Trochetiopsis ebenus

C Mountains: life in a cold climate

The Mountains house displays both horticultural alpines (dwarf plants and cultivars with particular cultivation requirements) and 'true' alpines, highly specialised species adapted to survive in severe montane climates.

Traditional sand plunges flank the house displaying seasonal interest plants at their peak, including in late spring, species tulips, fritillaries and European saxifrages, three of the Garden's nine National Collections®. A central, lozenge-shaped bed of tufa, a soft, porous, water-deposited rock easily penetrated by roots seeking anchorage and moisture, provides a variety of growing niches.

In the southern part of the house, there is a low naturalistic limestone landscape offering a diversity of micro-climates into which are grouped the principal alpine forms: cushions, mats, tufts, bulbs and dwarf shrubs.

Tulipa orphanidea

Tropaeolum tricolor

Fritillaria elwesii

D Tropical Rainforests: a hotbed of competition

The central Palm House and its adjoining wings are dedicated to Tropical Rainforests where the intense competition for resources, especially light, gives rise to a high, dense canopy and dark forest floor.

Overhead the canopy is studded with flamboyant orchids, bromeliads including the strange Spanish moss, *Tillandsia usneoides*, exotic passionflowers, and many climbing plants. In spring, the flowering of the jade vine, *Strongylodon macrobotrys*, is a breath-taking sight as a curtain of metre-long, jade-coloured inflorescences descends from the canopy.

The Tropical Rainforests display also features many important economic crops, for example rice, tea, coffee, cotton, rubber and mahogany, and some more unusual ones such as kapok and star fruit. These are mostly clustered around a central fishpool, a popular highlight with younger visitors.

On hot days the temperature can soar to over 40°C and the air becomes completely saturated with water, mimicking the humid tropical regions of the world.

Thunbergia mysorensis

Zingiber spectabile

Passiflora racemosa

E Carnivores: plants that bite back

Carnivorous plants grow in nutrient-poor environments especially lacking in nitrogen, and so obtain their nutrition from capturing prey, mostly insects. Carnivory in plants has evolved separately several times in unrelated plant groups. There are many different methods to trap prey: sticky leaf hairs in sundews, *Drosera*; sticky leaf surfaces in butterworts, *Pinguicula*; and, pitfall traps in pitcher plants, *Sarracenia*. They all require lime- and nutrient-poor water so must be maintained using rain water.

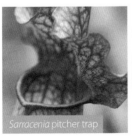
Sarracenia pitcher trap

Dionaea muscipula

Sarracenia flower

F Arid Lands: water vessels of the desert

Water is scarce in arid lands. Most arid places get small amounts of rain every year, with many months, if not years, passing between rainfalls. It can also be scorching hot, up to 50°C in the daytime. The nights, however, can be freezing cold. These extreme conditions support an amazing variety of extraordinary plants.

Arid Lands is inspired by the vision of a dry riverbed: a paved path runs through a desert landscape, inviting a comparison between African plants on one side and the 'new world' plants of the Americas on the other.

Arid land plants show a variety of mechanisms to survive low and infrequent rainfall. Many, like aloes, are succulent and store water in fleshy leaves. Cacti store water in swollen stems. Many cacti are globe-shaped, which maximises the stem's water storing capacity, while minimising the surface area through which water evaporates. Leaves, if they are present at all, are often reduced to protective spines.

Comparing the plants in the African bed to those from the American deserts reveals a phenomenon called 'convergent evolution'. Plants in both these areas have experienced the same problems of limited water supply and high temperatures, and have, independently, evolved similar survival mechanisms. So for example, the succulent, tree-like *Euphorbia cooperi* from east Africa resembles the Mexican fence post cactus, *Pachycereus marginatus*, opposite, although they are entirely unrelated.

Echinopsis oxygona   *Rebutia fiebrigii*   *Echinocactus grusonii*

G Life Before Flowers: a green world

Turn sharply left upon exiting the Glasshouse Range to find a shady house tucked behind its north side. This Life Before Flowers display explores the land plant groups which evolved earlier than the flowering plants which now dominate our planet.

Plant life before flowers consisted mainly of the liverworts, mosses, club-mosses, ferns and their relatives. These non-flowering plants are all dependent on water to complete their life-cycles since they all have swimming sperm. These houses are therefore kept damp and shady to allow reproduction to occur.

Outside this house, a green grove of hardy ferns and representatives of other ancient plant lineages has been recently planted to extend the display.

A maidenhair fern, *Adiantum x mariesii*

The piri-piri burr, *Acaena inermis*

Terrace Garden

To continue the theme of drama of diversity that unites the Glasshouse Range and nearby Bays in an exploration of some of the world's unique floras, the Terrace Garden has undergone a major renovation to present the flora of New Zealand.

The islands comprising New Zealand are deeply isolated in both geography and in time. New Zealand was once part of the supercontinent, Gondwana, which began to break up around 180 million years ago, distributing plant families across the southern hemisphere. A rich and unique flora has evolved in this isolation, encouraged in its diversification by a wealth of different natural habitats ranging from frost-free lowland forests of sub-tropical plants to icy, mountainous regions supporting alpine plants. The flora is correspondingly rich in endemic plants, with 85% of the species found naturally nowhere else in the world, accounting for the very distinct feel to the landscape.

This planting makes good use of the many niches and levels of the Terrace Garden; a north-facing, shady and damp cove for ferns occupies the sunken heart of the Terrace Garden, while stands of mountain flax, *Phormium cookianum*, dominate the southern perimeter.

The Bee Borders

The beautiful double Bee Borders in front of the Glasshouse Range have been created with some of the flowers bees love best and are abuzz from spring through to autumn with the insects busy harvesting nectar and pollen. But the Bee Borders are also a honeypot for visitors, as the chief characteristic that makes a flower attractive to bees also makes them excellent garden plants – lots of brightly-coloured flowers on sturdy plants. In this case they are massed in an exhilarating 'cottage garden' style.

Bees visit flowers for food: nectar provides sugars for energy, while some bee species collect pollen for proteins essential to growth. In doing so, bees transport pollen between flowers and effect pollination. Many good bee plants have large, tubular flowers symmetrical along the vertical axis (as we are). The lower petal is often extended or lipped to provide a landing platform for the visiting bee. This specialised petal is also decorated with lines or spots, called nectar guides, that show the way to the nectar reward within. Common foxgloves, *Digitalis purpurea*, are a good example of this, and are used extensively in the planting along with snapdragon, *Antirrhinum majus*, and viper's bugloss, *Echium vulgare*.

The colour scheme for the Bee Borders is a soft haze of blues, mauves and violets, as bees can see this part of the colour spectrum best. Bees can even see a colour invisible to the human eye called bee ultra-violet, often present in nectar guides. They are unable, however, to see bright red – one of the reasons red is absent from the planting scheme. Red flowers are associated with bird pollinators.

Gardeners can play an important role in helping bee populations stay healthy by including some of these beautiful flowers in their own planting schemes to provide a rich food source. Most of the bee plants in these borders are readily available from garden centres and nurseries, and many are straightforward to raise from seed.

The Bee Borders in late spring, with *Anchusa*, *Allium* and foxglove, *Digitalis*

The coppery new leaves on the Cambridge oak, *Quercus* x *warburgii* break through in May

Gilbert-Carter Memorial Area

This informal arboretum area commemorates Humphrey Gilbert-Carter, the Garden's first academic Director from 1919-1951. His great love was catkin-bearing trees, which feature strongly in this woodland and meadow planting. In the heart of the woodland is a fine specimen of the Cambridge oak, *Quercus* x *warburgii*. It is a marvellous sight in May when the leathery over-wintered leaves are finally shed, the new coppery-red foliage unfurls, and the tree is festooned with tasseled bunches of golden-yellow catkins.

By late spring, the trees are lapped by a sea of foaming cow parsley, *Anthriscus sylvestris*, a superb foil for flowering trees such as the Judas tree, *Cercis siliquastrum*, with its magenta pea-like flowers bursting straight from the bare branches and trunk.

The meandering mown paths connect many intimate glades of flowering shrubs and small trees, where there is much to discover particularly early in the year. Here the February-flowering Cornelian cherry, *Cornus mas*, with its masses of tiny yellow flowers gives way to the striking white bracts of *Cornus* 'Eddie's White Wonder' and the chalky-white flowers of the Chinese bitter orange, *Poncirus trifoliata*, borne on spiny green stems. The southern boundary of the woodland has a sinuous tangle of pale-blue flowered Chinese wisteria, *Wisteria sinensis*, pruned into free-standing shapes, backed by the deeply-fissured bark of the unusual tree honeysuckle, *Lonicera maackii*. Later in the summer, the Kentucky yellowwood, *Cladrastis kentukea*, is a spectacular sight, with long racemes of fragrant white flowers fluttering in the lightest breeze. On the south side, the Japanese pagoda tree, *Styphnolobium japonicum*, bears creamy flowers, flushed peachy-yellow, in profuse airy panicles. It flowers long after most other ornamental trees have finished their displays, in late summer to early autumn. British and European *Sorbus* species dominate the south-eastern quarter. Many of these are extremely rare and of great conservation value.

The catchfly, *Silene conica*, is a threatened Breckland plant

British Wild Plants

The Garden's collections of British wild plants are distributed across the Limestone Mound and the Fen Display opposite.

The Limestone Mound demonstrates some of the huge array of British wild plants that can be found on chalk and limestone (calcareous) soils. One of the most spectacular sites in May and June is the tumbling display of sulphur-yellow rock-roses, *Helianthemum*, combining with the lovely deep-blue flowers of purple gromwell, *Lithospermum purpureocaeruleum,* rare in the UK. This plant thrives here and spreads by tip rooting, like a bramble, an unusual characteristic.

On top of the mound is a massed planting of native shrubs and trees typical of chalk and limestone areas. Amongst them is a large and thriving *Sorbus bristoliensis,* endemic to the Avon Gorge near Bristol, with an estimated wild population of 100 trees. The Botanic Garden has a good collection of these beautiful wild *Sorbus* species in the Gilbert-Carter Memorial Area.

A chalk grassland habitat is represented on the eastern face of the mound and features rare annuals such as candytuft, *Iberis amara*, with white flowers. There is a nice population of an as yet unidentified eyebright, *Euphrasia* species, a semiparasitic plant with small white flowers and lilac lip. In spring look for the pasque flower, *Pulsatilla vulgaris,* a purple-flowered relative of the buttercup, which is the county flower of Cambridgeshire.

A special display focuses on Breckland plants from the borders of Cambridgeshire, Suffolk and Norfolk, a unique region of blown sand overlying chalk. Before the use of fertilisers became widespread in modern agriculture, fertility was restored by allowing fields to lie fallow every few years. These 'brecks' (fallow fields) supported unique and now-threatened plants such as the catchfly, *Silene conica*, and the Breckland speedwell, *Veronica triphyllos*, which is very rare and known at only two or three sites in the wild.

The western slope of the mound has plants typical of the woodlands which develop on boulder clay containing large quantities of chalk, such as the ancient woods of Hayley Wood and Buff Wood in west Cambridgeshire. The graceful wood melick, *Melica uniflora* f. *albida*, a white-bracted mutant, clothes the mound in soft grass in late spring. Plants of shady limestone are found on the northern side of the mound, such as the magnificent spires of the large bellflower, *Campanula latifolia*.

The Fen Display opposite seeks to tell the story of the region to the north of Cambridge, which was once a vast plant-rich fen through which the rivers Ouse and Nene meandered. Over the last 350 years, the Fens have been reduced through drainage to just a few, scattered pockets.

The Fens receive little rainfall, but water from the Midlands and East Anglia filters through the surrounding rocks and collects in this low-lying area. The Fen Display demonstrates the transition in the vegetation from deep open water with water lilies through reedbed and wet margins to woodland (Fen carr), which consists mainly of birches and willows. This range of habitats from deep water to drier margins supports a rich and varied flora, easily accessed via the boardwalk. The visually dominant plants are swathes of common reed, *Phragmites australis*, and bulrush or reedmace, *Typha latifolia*, with vivid splashes of colour coming from purple loosestrife, *Lythrum salicaria*, and rich fragrance from meadowsweet, *Filipendula ulmaria*. Many Fen specialties are represented including the rare Cambridge milk parsley, *Selinum carvifolia*, the Fen ragwort, *Senecio paludosus*, thought to have been extinct in nature for over a century until its chance rediscovery in 1972, and the 'non-stinging' stinging nettle, *Urtica dioica* subsp. *galeopsifolia* (please note, this is not reliably 'non-stinging'!).

Each quadrant of the Fen Display reedbed is cut once every four years to mimic traditional management techniques.

Fen Display in late summer

...ng for newts in the Fen Display

Red campion, *Silene dioica*

The Limestone Mound in early summer with rock-roses, *Helianthemum*

Echinacea 'White Swan', a late summer emergent, with *Geranium* 'Brookside'

Cory Lawn

Cory Lawn was carved from the Garden to set off Cory Lodge, designed by influential Cambridge architect, Mackay Baillie Scott in an arts and crafts style. The Lodge was built in 1924-5 as the Director's residence and named to honour Reginald Cory, an alumnus of Trinity College and life-long benefactor of the Garden, who financed its construction.

Cory Lawn has variously been a tennis court and pasture for the pet donkey of a former Director's family! As part of the Sainsbury Laboratory project, a new landscape was created to become the harmonising principle between the heritage architecture of Cory Lodge and the contemporary approach of the Sainsbury Laboratory.

The large central grass lawn is retained to set off Cory Lodge, but the sloped lawn flanks have been re-graded and segmented by rectangular tables of yew, clipped at differing heights into interlocking geometric shapes. This approach is echoed in the line of five table-top pruned limes, *Tilia henryana*, that grace the adjacent Café terrace. This strong design reflects both the structural formalism of the Sainsbury Laboratory and frames Cory Lodge.

In contrast, the herbaceous plantings are informal and exuberant. A base matrix of grasses, ferns and ground-covering perennials is punctuated by flowering emergents to provide an ever-changing palette of colour and form through the year. Snowdrops and tulips are followed by irises, salvias, and late-flowering red-hot pokers and asters, all against a foil of billowing foliage and grasses. Even in winter, the architectural stems and spent flowerheads of the summer perennials extend the season, rimed with frost. To reflect the different conditions around the rectangle of Cory Lawn, two base matrices are used - one for shade, the other for sun.

The new design provides for some impressive trees including a young *Quercus pubescens*, banked up by a rusted steel retaining wall. Adjacent to Cory Lodge, there is a superb specimen of Western catalpa, *Catalpa speciosa*, an Indian bean tree relative from North America, with white flowers followed by long slender fruits. On the north wall of the house is a maidenhair tree, *Ginkgo biloba*, trained as an espalier since 1987, as a nod to the two magnificent specimens trained up the walls of the Department of Plant Sciences on the Downing Site, the leaf of which is the logo of the Garden's mother department.

Geranium x cantabrigiense 'Biokovo'

Grasses are a key element of the base planting matrix for Cory Lawn

Table-top pruned limes, *Tilia henryana*, will be trained to provide shade to the Garden Café terrace

gium planum with *Origanum laevigatum* 'Herrenhausen'

Dry Garden

Water is a precious resource locally and globally. Cambridge's climate is classified as 'semi-arid', which has inspired the Dry Garden, a beautiful, water-wise planting suitable for a typical south-facing back garden in the City.

We have imposed a permanent hosepipe ban in the Dry Garden, but it nevertheless flourishes. This has been achieved principally through selecting plants that can survive short-term drought. Appropriate horticultural techniques are displayed, such as applying thick, moisture-conserving inorganic mulches and planting closely to help reduce loss of water from the soil.

Of the 100 different species that thrive here, many are Mediterranean natives such as lavender, thyme and blue spurge, *Euphorbia myrsinites*. Commonly, drought-tolerant plants have small leaves that reduce water-loss. They can be silvery and reflect heat, or hairy and trap moisture. Bulbs and annuals both demonstrate life-cycles that avoid summer drought and are featured strongly. Bulbs flower, die down and survive as underground storage organs through the summer, while annuals grow, flower and set seed early in the year to ensure the next generation in the space of just a few months. There are also a number of British endemics included, on the basis of many years observation of what grows easily in the Botanic Garden. These include stinking iris, *Iris foetidissima*, and even the male fern, *Dryopteris filix-mas*.

A pergola forms the backdrop to the Dry Garden and is draped with drought-tolerant climbers such as *Clematis armandii* and purple grape vine, *Vitis vinifera* 'Purpurea', that provide light shade for the table and chairs here. This affords the perfect spot from which to take notes on how to incorporate water-wise gardening into your own garden at home.

Rosa 'Mme de la Roche-Lambert'

Rose Garden

The origin of our modern garden roses was a mystery until the 20th century. From 1922-1947, their genealogy was explored by geneticist Charles Chamberlain Hurst here in the Botanic Garden. Hurst attempted to disentangle their complex ancestry by crossing rose species and examining the chromosomes of the resulting hybrids. He proposed a scheme of rose evolution from these studies.

This is demonstrated in the design of the Rose Garden, the work of legendary plantsman and Garden Adviser to the National Trust, Graham Stuart Thomas, who was a horticultural trainee here. The Rose Garden straddles the South Walk: on the south side are the rose species and the primary hybrids arising between them. The radiating island beds on the north side show the ancestral European roses, crosses that gave rise to groups including Damask, Bourbons and hybrid Gallicas and the key influence of the China roses that brought repeat flowering and new colours. The Rose Garden was planted in 1980-81 to celebrate the 150th anniversary of the University acquiring the land for a 'new' Botanic Garden in 1831.

The garden forms of roses do not grow particularly well in the chalky, dry soil of the Botanic Garden, so a thick mulch is applied each autumn to enrich the soil and conserve moisture. Species and primary hybrids, however, flourish. Hurst created many beautiful hybrids during his experimental work and he named two after the Botanic Garden – the single pink *Rosa* 'Cantab' and the beautiful yellow shrub *Rosa* x *cantabrigiensis*. Another hybrid commemorates the Botanic Garden benefactor Reginald Cory, and is known as *R.* x *coryana*.

The diversity of colour and form of the many different roses in the Rose Garden is counterbalanced by a classic underplanting of lavender and geranium so throughout the summer, the Rose Garden is a magnet not just for visitors but for myriad bees and butterflies. At its heart are two back-to-back, yew-enclosed benches that offer scent-infused vantage points over the history of the garden rose.

The 'walls' of the maze are planted with the New Zealand grass, *Anemanthele lessoniana*

Grass Maze

Turf mazes were a common feature of villages in medieval England. The 'walls' of our grass maze are grown from the New Zealand bunch grass, *Anemanthele lessoniana*. A tactile grass that turns a lovely bronze in late summer, it rustles and sways in the gentlest breeze, and makes for a very inviting racetrack that is perennially popular with children.

As a bunch grass, new shoots arise from inside the clump rather than by new growth spreading away from the centre. This helps the maze resist the onslaught of umpteen races to the centre but, nevertheless, we have to replant the maze at least every other year so occasionally it is unavailable.

Close by is another planting that children find intriguing: Healthy Herbie is a person-shaped bed stocked with plants either being researched for potential use in a licensed medical drug or already used in the production of such medicines.

This Savoy cabbage, *Brassica oleracea* Captitata group, is descended from the wild cabbage, a maritime cliff plant

Genetics Garden

The extraordinary diversity of plants arises from differences in their genetic constitution, coupled with the way in which these combinations of genes control the development of the plant from seed to mature form.

Modern wheats derive from a cross between an early cultivated wheat and a wild goat grass, *Aegilops tauschii*, about 8,000 years ago in farmers' fields in northern Iran. The genetic constitution of the goat grass gave bread wheat tolerance to cold and wet. As seed of this hardier strain of bread wheat was selected generation after generation, arable farming spread into the colder temperate regions of the world from its centre of origin in the Middle East. It now accounts for over 95% of wheat grown worldwide.

For thousands of years, humans have developed a whole range of crop varieties with different uses by selecting variations arising within single species such as wild cabbage, *Brassica oleracea*, or wild beet, *Beta vulgaris*. In nature, the wild cabbage is a maritime cliff plant rather like kale. Artificial selection of different genetic combinations has given rise to varieties as diverse as Brussel sprouts, red cabbage, cauliflower and kohlrabi, in which the development of different parts of the plant has been altered. Wild beet was probably first brought into cultivation by the Romans who used it as a leaf vegetable. Selections have given rise to spinach beet, beetroot, sugar beet and rhubarb chard. The Genetics Garden shows many of these selection stories, so by late summer the display resembles a well-tended allotment!

Genetics and plant breeding continues to have dramatic effects on our flower gardens and a display of double flowers (*flore pleno*) is in development, comparing them with their single equivalents. The genetics of how a leafy shoot is converted into a flower (all the sepals, petals and sexual parts are, in fact, transformed leaves) is complex and offers insight into how combinations of genes interact to produce different plants you can grow in your garden.

The shrubby honeysuckle, *Lonicera elisae*

Winter Garden

The Winter Garden brings together coloured stems, bark and foliage texture with winter flower and fragrance. Above all, the handling of light is crucial for the success of the overall design. The level site was landscaped to create a shallow valley through which runs a gently curving path. The site is open to the south so that precious winter sunlight can flood in.

Enticing fragrance bathes the entrances to the Winter Garden, which are planted with combinations of the lemon meringue-scented honeysuckle *Lonicera* x *purpusii*, many intoxicating *Viburnum* species and pale pink *Daphne bholua* ' Jacqueline Postill'. The scooping out of the site means that the scents gather and intensify rather than disperse.

Stripes of dogwoods, *Cornus sericea* 'Flaviramea', with its brilliant yellow-green winter stems and its red-stemmed relative, *Cornus alba* 'Sibirica' cut across the Winter Garden. The setting sun illuminates this swathe, coming to rest on the brilliant orange stems of pollarded scarlet willow, *Salix alba* 'Chermesina'. These are pruned hard back by April to stimulate brilliantly coloured new growth for the next season.

Trees have been chosen for winter blossom or for striking bark patterns – the mottled snakeskin bark of *Acer capillipes*, the rich amber-coloured paper peelings of paperbark maple, *Acer griseum*, and the shiny pink, buff and yellow bark of *Betula albosinensis* var. *septentrionalis*. Combinations of densely-planted bulbs including golden winter aconites, *Eranthis hyemalis*, and snowdrops provide an excellent food source in February for any bees tempted out by warm weather. Great tangles of many different ornamental thorns, from the rusty-red, bristled Japanese wineberry, *Rubus phoenicolasius*, to ghostly white *Rubus biflorus* are an unusual and dramatic feature. The leathery leaves of *Bergenia* species add deep maroon tones to many planting vignettes, in particular to combinations of snowdrop and *Carex*.

The Winter Garden was designed in 1979 by Peter Orriss and Norman Villis, Superintendent and Garden Supervisor at the Garden respectively.

A frosty icing to the Winter Garden sharpens the colouring

Spiny bear's breeches, *Acanthus spinosus*, was introduced from Southern Europe in 1629

Chronological Bed

For thousands of years, people have introduced plants to the British Isles from all over the globe for interest, pleasure or for economic gain, and our gardens have been greatly enriched by this diversity as a result. The Chronological Bed is a linear, mainly herbaceous planting, which puts these plant introductions into a time-frame.

The border begins at the east end with a group of plants known to have been introduced to Britain from Roman times up to the 16th century. As we come towards the present day, more accurate documentation has allowed plant introductions to be grouped into 20-year periods.

What emerges is a picture of British geopolitical and economic interest over the last 500 years, as the Americas, South Africa, India and China in succession provided new species for consumption, medicinal drugs or for ornamental gardens. Plant-hunting activity reached fever pitch towards the end of 19th century. It powered the expansion of the British Empire by redistributing economic crops to new parts of its dominions, but also changed the plants in British gardens and parks as new ornamental species were introduced.

The Chronological Bed allows a glimpse as to which plants may have featured in a medieval garden, for example, but it is interesting to see just how recently some of our garden stalwarts have been introduced: the popular and freely-seeding lady's mantle, *Alchemilla mollis*, with its froth of acid green flowers, only arrived at the end of the 19th century.

The Chronological Bed was conceived by John Gilmour, Director of the Botanic Garden from 1951-1973.

Crocosmia 'Lucifer' ensures sizzling late summer colour

Herbaceous Beds

The Herbaceous Beds at the eastern end of the Fairway illustrate the wealth of perennial species available to the gardener. The beds are spectacular throughout the summer and into the autumn, with magnificent displays of bold, dramatic plants.

These include the beautiful coral feathers of plume poppy, *Macleaya microcarpa*, its glaucous foliage also providing a cool foil to vivid late summer combinations of monkshood, *Aconitum carmichaelii* 'Kelmscott', jewel-coloured *Penstemon*, the perennial sunflower *Helianthus salicifolius* 'Lemon Queen', coneflower, *Rudbeckia triloba* and many *Sedum* and *Salvia* species. The elegant silver grass, *Miscanthus sinensis* 'Gracillimus', provides shimmering movement and texture.

The Herbaceous Beds are bordered on one side by a varied collection of the genus *Viburnum*, many of which are richly-scented and provide interest throughout the year. They include valuable evergreens such as *Viburnum rhytidophyllum* and *V. tinus*, as well as the winter-flowering deciduous species *V. x bodnantense*, and its parents, which provide vital cheer and scent in the darkest months. In spring, *Viburnum* x *burkwoodii* and its parents *V. carlesii* and *V. utile*, contribute great white snowballs of sweetly-scented flowers, followed by the early summer-flowering *V. plicatum*.

The boundary with Hills Road was remodelled in 2012 when poor trees were removed and replaced with specimen silver lime trees, *Tilia tomentosa*, to create a new screen for the coming century. To this backbone, rare limes from China and elsewhere have been added – part of a research collection on this important tree group.

Herbs are a major element of the Scented Garden

Scented Garden

Plants produce a great array of aromatic substances. Leaf aromas encompass mint, lemon, rose and even curry, while strongly scented flowers attract pollinating insects.

The Scented Garden was designed in 1960 to perfume the air and stimulate our sense of smell. To help collect and intensify the scents, the site was excavated to create a protected well. Along the north side of the plot, the planting bed is raised so that visitors can encounter the scented foliage and flowers at close range, including early bulbs such as pheasant eye narcissus, *Narcissus poeticus*, and hyacinth. The Scented Garden underwent a major overhaul in 2008 when some over-dominant shrubs were removed in order to diversify the plantings. Cushions of herbs are used to create a textured base for choice shrub roses, including *Rosa* 'Scepter'd Isle'.

The Scented Garden is fragrant even in the depths of winter with the rich, exotic notes of wintersweet, *Chimonanthus praecox*, and the vanilla of *Viburnum farreri*. In the summer, the wooden shelter in the heart of the Scented Garden is bathed in the sweet lemon of *Rosa* 'Seagull' which is being trained across its roof. Annual plants include old varieties of sweet pea, *Lathyrus odoratus*, scrambling up willow wigwams and many scented ornamental tobacco plants, *Nicotiana*. Scented-leaf pelargoniums are included for texture and for the sharp scents released when the foliage is lightly brushed.

Autumn Garden

As the days shorten and the temperatures drop in the autumn months, spectacular leaf colour ignites the Botanic Garden as the dominating green chlorophyll breaks down. The fiery colours of the Autumn Garden, from vivid coral to deep purple, combine with late flowers, seedheads, fruits and feathery grasses to become a beautiful, richly textured tapestry.

Some of the best displays of autumn foliage are provided by two sweetgums, *Liquidambar styraciflua* 'Worplesdon' and *L. orientalis* from Turkey. The latter species, although rarely grown, is a valuable late colourer and the decaying, star-shaped leaves take on glowing deep-orange tones. This very effective sweetgum duo is repeated on the Lake's northern shore.

The oval, often blotched foliage of many different smokebushes, *Cotinus*, contribute flaming reds, pink, clarets and oranges against which the pale grey or coral smudges of the spent inflorescences drift. Other autumn leaf colour comes from many acer species, including a striking trio of Japanese maples, *Acer palmatum* 'Osakazuki'. The palmate, seven-lobed leaves are wine-red, each leaf held on a slender, cerise-pink stalk as are the samara fruits – a pair of seeds held in papery burgundy wings. They make a vibrant contrast to the butter-yellow, fan-shaped foliage of a neighbouring maidenhair tree, *Ginkgo biloba*. The soft, feathery foliage of a dawn redwood, *Metasequoia glyptostroboides*, turns a coppery russet, a lovely upward sweep of fox-fur against a cushion of glaucous evergreens.

The magnificent black walnut, *Juglans nigra*, is one of the Garden's finest trees

Trees

CITY
CENTRE
¾ mile

Brookside Gate

BATEMAN STREET

park ride
stop
Trumpington

Brookside
Lawn

Leguminosae
(pea family : false acacia, laburnum, Juda

Magnoliaceae
(magnolias, tulip trees)

Juglandaceae
(walnuts, wingnuts)

LYNCH WALK

Aceraceae
(maples)

WEST WALK

HENSLOW WALK

Main Lawn

Conifers

Hippocastanaceae
(horse chestnuts, buckeyes)

MAIN WALK

TRUMPINGTON ROAD (A134)

Tiliaceae
(limes)

WEST WALK

HENSLOW WALK

Ulmaceae
(elms)

SOUTH WALK

Moraceae
(mulberrys)

Oleaceae
(olive family : ash, forsythias, lilacs)

Hamamelidaceae
(witchhazel family and relatives: ironwoods)

BROOKLANDS AVENUE

1 2 3 4 5 6 7 8 9 10 11 12 13 14 15 16 17 20

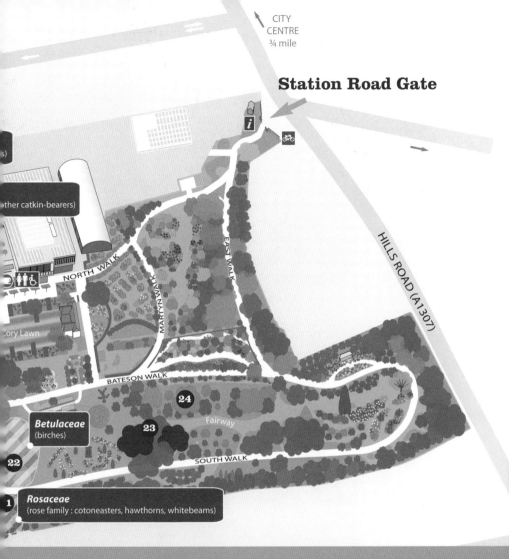

CITY CENTRE ¾ mile

Station Road Gate

i

NORTH WALK

EAST WALK

MARTYN WALK

HILLS ROAD (A1307)

ory Lawn

ther catkin-bearers)

BATESON WALK

24

Betulaceae
(birches)

23

Fairway

22

SOUTH WALK

1 *Rosaceae*
(rose family : cotoneasters, hawthorns, whitebeams)

ac Newton's apple tree
lans nigra (black walnut)
rocarya fraxinifolia (Caucasian gnut)
r pseudoplatanus (sycamore)
r sempervirens (Cretan maple)
culus californica (Californian keye)
tasequoia glyptostroboides (dawn wood)

8: *Pinus nigra* (black pine)
9: *Tiliaceae* (lime) family
10: *Maclura pomifera* (Osage orange)
11: *Parrotia persica* (Persian ironwood)
12: *Cercis siliquastrum* (Judas tree)
13: *Gleditsia sinensis* (Chinese honey locust) & *Cladrastis kentukea* (Kentucky yellowwood)
14: *Cedrus libani* (cedar of Lebanon)
15: *Sequoiadendron giganteum* (giant redwood)

16: *Pinus gerardiana* (Gerard's pine)
17: *Quercus suber* (cork oak)
18: *Fagus sylvatica* (common beech)
19: *Pinus monophylla* (single-leaved nut pine)
20: *Quercus* x *warburgii* (Cambridge oak)
21: *Pyrus communis* (wild pear)
22: *Alnus subcordata* (Caucasian alder)
23: *Fraxinus ornus* (manna ash)
24: *Catalpa* sp (Indian bean trees)

The autumn foliage of the dawn redwood, *Metasequoia glyptostroboides*

Trees form the backbone of the Botanic Garden and represent one of the best collections in the region. They play an important role enclosing the site to create a green oasis in the City and provide year-round interest, from structural tracery and textured barks in winter through spring and summer flowering to the autumn colour that ignites the Garden.

Some of our trees are the finest specimens in the UK and have 'champion' status; others are heritage trees, noteworthy for the stories they tell. You can find many of these in the older, western part of the Garden where the collections are arranged systematically in families. The development of the eastern half of the Botanic Garden from the 1950s has allowed thematic or ornamental groupings to be created, for example the fiery tapestry of the Autumn Garden.

The establishment of a major tree collection was the vision of John Stevens Henslow, Professor of Botany at the University from 1825-61 and founder of this Botanic Garden. In his presentation to the University, Henslow stated: 'The reason why a modern Botanic Garden requires so much larger space than formerly is chiefly owing to the vastly increased number of trees and shrubs that have been introduced in the last half century.'

We maintain an active tree-planting policy to safeguard our status as a major arboretum. A particular focus at the moment is trialling species from hotter climates for the future.

1. Isaac Newton's apple tree

This compact apple tree is a selection called 'Flower of Kent' and is a scion of the original tree at Woolsthorpe Manor, Lincolnshire, the family home of Cambridge scientist, Sir Isaac Newton. It is said that Newton was inspired to formulate his theory of gravity by watching an apple fall from the Woolsthorpe tree. Newton published his theory, without the apple anecdote, in his *Principia* in 1687.

2. *Juglans nigra* (black walnut)

This magnificent black walnut, is one of the Garden's original trees. In 1915, Curator Richard Lynch noted that the black walnut was one of the finest in the British Isles. At close to 25 metres tall, this remains true approaching a century later. It is rare for specimens to attain this stature, even in its native United States, since most are felled for the highly-prized timber. The deeply furrowed bark, large pinnate leaves that turn a warm butter yellow in autumn, and vast, domed crown, are amongst its outstanding features.

3. *Pterocarya fraxinifolia* (Caucasian wingnut)

The stand of Caucasian wingnut that straddles the stream feeding the Lake is one of the outstanding features of the Garden. Originally it consisted of two trees, now long lost, from which an immense thicket has grown up.

One of the best times to admire the trees is in July when the pendant, plait-like green catkins elongate before developing their winged fruits. Like the nearby *Platycarya strobilacea* on Brookside Lawn, the Caucasian wingnut is a reminder that the *Juglandaceae* family used to be much more diverse. At present, species such as walnuts and hickories, with edible fruits dispersed by animals, are predominant, while the wind-dispersed species like the Caucasian wingnut are considered more unusual.

4. *Acer pseudoplatanus* (sycamore)

The sycamore is a hardy tree abundant all over Britain, although opinions diverge as to when it was introduced. The Botanic Garden's fine specimen stands by Hobson's Conduit, the man-made river dating from 1610 that brings fresh water into the City and forms the western boundary of the Garden.

5. *Acer sempervirens* (Cretan maple)

The Cretan maple is native to the eastern Mediterranean and is one of the most drought-tolerant species in the genus, occurring on dry, sunny hillsides. This explains why it has done well in Cambridge, where rainfall is low and the soil free-draining. Although a slow-grower, the Garden's tree has nevertheless reached an impressive 10 metres. The small leaves are dark green, glossy and three-lobed, creating a dense cover.

6. *Aesculus californica* (Californian buckeye)

The Californian buckeye is one of the most spectacular flowering trees in the Garden. Usually blooming from mid-June, it is a low, wide-spreading, multi-trunked tree which bears a profusion of erect white flower spikes up to 20cm long. It clearly enjoys the

Cambridge climate and our trees are amongst the best in the country. The largest specimen can be found by the Main Gate. A second tree, located close to the Grass Maze, was collected by the great plantsman and former Botanic Garden horticultural trainee, Roy Lancaster.

7 *Metasequoia glyptostroboides* (dawn redwood)

The dawn redwood was discovered in 1941 in a remote Schezuan village in central China. The first consignment of seed to head west reached the Arnold Arboretum, United States, in January 1948. However, the seed from which our specimen was grown came directly from China to Cambridge, meaning this tree was the first dawn redwood to be planted on British soil.

The beautiful ferny foliage is light green in spring and turns pink and copper in autumn before being shed to reveal a strong pyramidal winter silhouette. It prefers a damp habitat, hence its position close to the Lake edge where it is paired with its closest living relative, the swamp cypress, *Taxodium distichum*, from the United States and Mexico, which grows directly out of the Lake bed. It is also a deciduous conifer, turning deep orange in autumn, and is notable for its distinctive knobbly pneumatophores (the 'knees') rising out of the water.

8. *Pinus nigra* (black pine)

The black pines, along the Main Walk, group together subspecies displaying distinctive features, and date from the earliest plantings of the 1840s. The most extreme contrast is the pairing of *Pinus nigra* subsp. *nigra* with *P. nigra* subsp. *salzmannii* planted directly opposite each other on the Main Walk.

The former, from snowy regions of Austria, has downward-sloping, relatively unbranched, slender limbs with short, stiff needles, while *P. nigra* subsp. *salzmannii* from Spain has a flat, spreading and open canopy with long needles. The positioning of such different growth forms in this high-profile and formal spot, where more usually symmetry would be called for, has a didactic purpose. Nearby are found two further subspecies, the Crimean pine, *P. nigra* subsp. *pallasiana*, and the Corsican pine, *P. nigra* subsp. *laricio*. These black pines reveal how deeply Henslow was already engaged in trying to determine the nature of species by assessing variation in and between plant species.

Into this rich research environment came the young Charles Darwin. He spent so much time in the company of his teacher and mentor that he became known amongst the dons as 'the man who walks with Henslow'. This close relationship led to Henslow recommending Darwin for the position of naturalist on HMS Beagle. His Cambridge experience and the five-year voyage played pivotal roles in the genesis of Darwin's revolutionary thinking, which led to *On the Origin of Species*, published in 1859.

9. *Tiliaceae* (lime) family

The common lime, *Tilia europaea*, at the western end of the Main Walk was planted in November 1846 by the Vice Chancellor of the University of Cambridge, Reverend Ralph Tatham, to mark the opening of the 'new' Botanic Garden. Its leaf has become the Garden's logo. In summer, as the breeze blows, the air is saturated with sweet scent and the silver limes, *Tilia tomentosa*, add an argent accent to the treescape as the silvery undersides of the leaves turn uppermost. Choice limes can also be found in the Gilbert Carter Memorial Area, off the South Walk, and along the Hills Road boundary.

10. *Maclura pomifera* (Osage orange)

The Osage orange is one of the most unusual members of the mulberry family, *Moraceae*. This tree bears orange-sized fruit high up in the tree, but the autumn winds often bring them down to litter the grass beneath with large, deeply fissured, lurid neon green tennis balls, or as the horticultural staff call them, 'pickled gardeners' brains'! It is endemic to North America and named for the Osage Indians of Missouri. The Osage orange enjoys the Cambridge climate and ours is one of the best specimens in the country.

Close by, other members of the *Moraceae* are notable in autumn. The paper mullberrys, *Broussontia papyrifera* and *B. kazinoki* are rounded trees that for just a few weeks in the autumn bear very striking, globose fruits studded with orange, jelly-textured, finger-shaped protrusions, complete with fingernail indentations!

The Garden's example of the Mongolian mulberry, *Morus mongolica*, very rare in cultivation, is a champion tree. In autumn, the toothed, elliptic leaves turn a very deep

pairing of black pine subspecies, *Pinus nigra* subsp *salzmanii* on the left and *Pinus nigra* subsp nigra on the right

ocarya fraxinifolia

7 *Metasequoia glyptostroboides*

6 *Aesculus californica*

10 Fruits of *Broussonetia kazinoki* in the mulberry, *Moraceae*, family

purple, almost black. The white mulberry, *Morus alba*, which can also be found nearby, produces flavoursome fruit in autumn.

11. *Parrotia persica* (Persian ironwood)

Overlooking the Systematic Beds is a fine Persian ironwood in the witchhazel family, *Hamamelidaceae*. It is a native of the southern Caucasus and northern Iran and is named for its extremely hard wood. The flattened, spreading canopy is an intricate weave of self-grafted and fused branches in a beautiful palette of buff, pink and pearly grey. In winter, tiny male flowers, consisting of clusters of crimson stamens, appear directly from the bare, serpentine branches. In autumn, the oval, roughly-toothed leaves turn copper, gold and red, making this a truly year-round tree.

12. *Cercis siliquastrum* (Judas tree)

There are many fine examples of Judas trees around Cambridge, its enjoyment of the dry Cambridge climate bearing witness to its Mediterranean origins.

Richard Lynch, Curator, noted in 1915 that the specimen growing in the Gilbert-Carter Memorial Area was one of the finest in the country. The weight of its limbs has caused the tree to fall apart, as it is prone to do, and it is now a wonderful spreading specimen of great character. The startling, bright mauve, clusters of flowers are typical of the pea family, *Leguminosae*, and erupt, like blisters, along the bare branches in late spring, followed by long pods that persist well into winter.

13. *Gleditsia sinensis* (Chinese honey locust) & *Cladrastis kentukea* (Kentucky yellowwood)

The trunk of the impressive Chinese honey locust in the *Leguminosae* collection is heavily armoured with clusters of ferocious, branched spines. This tree lost its champion status when its top was removed in order to maintain its structural integrity. Great spotted woodpeckers often nest in a hollow branch.

In summer, the closeby Kentucky yellowwood, *Cladrastis kentukea*, produces fountains of long, white, scented flowers – a spectacular sight.

14. *Cedrus libani* (cedar of Lebanon)

At the crossroads of the Henslow Walk and Main Walk is the cavernous dome of an immense cedar of Lebanon. The prominent cones take a year to mature and can be seen in several stages of development from tightly closed egg-shaped cones held erectly along the branches, to the disintegrated basal rosettes strewn across the ground beneath.

15. *Sequoiadendron giganteum* (giant redwood)

The giant redwood was introduced from California by Cornish-born plant collector William Lobb. In 1852, he acted on a tip off and tracked down a stand of giant redwoods in Calaveras Grove. Recognising the market potential of this new find, Lobb cut short his trip and returned home. Within a year, Veitch's nursery was offering seedlings for sale and Cambridge University Botanic Garden was among the earliest recipients of these plants.

The two trees on opposite sides of the Main Walk near the Fountain are believed to be from Lobb's original collection and were planted out in 1855. Their magnificent pyramidal shapes introduce a dynamic vertical lift to the landscape, softened by the feathery foliage and studding of small cones. The soft, spongy, reddish bark acts as insulating fire protection and is irresistible to the touch.

16. *Pinus gerardiana* (Gerard's pine)

This is one of the 'plate-bark pines', referring to its beautiful tiled, plated bark. Our tree is a champion tree at 14.4 metres high, and no other specimen in the British Isles appears to have grown so well.

In the wild, it grows in the Himalayas, often in association with the blue pine, *Pinus wallichiana*, and the deodar cedar, *Cedrus deodara*, both of which you will find along the Main Walk.

17. *Quercus suber* (cork oak)

Located at the eastern end of the Glasshouse Range is a majestic cork oak, contradicting its reputation for poor growth in England. In its natural habitat, the spongy, corky bark protects the tree from fire; it is also harvested for wine corks and

18 A weeping form of the common beech, *Fagus sylvatica*

13 *Cladrastis kentukea*

11 Natural branch grafting in Persian ironwood, *Parrotia persica*

12 *Cercis siliquastrum*

24 *Catalpa speciosa*

other products. The tree remains consistently evergreen throughout all but the very coldest Cambridge winters.

It grows next to a hybrid offspring, the Fulham oak, *Quercus* × *hispanica*. The hybrid inherited the rapid growth rate of one parent, the Turkey oak, *Quercus cerris*, but also the thickly fissured bark, evergreen foliage and form of *Quercus suber*.

18. *Fagus sylvatica* (common beech)

At the western edge of Cory Lodge lawn, within the plantings of catkin-bearing trees, stands a common beech surrounded by variants. Adjacent is a lovely cut-leaved beech, *Fagus sylvatica* 'Laciniata', displaying narrow, deeply-cut feathery leaves. Another has upward-turning tips to its long thin branches, while an outstanding weeping beech cascades over the path and turns bright copper in the autumn. A graft join is clearly visible some 1.5 metres clear of the ground, where the weeping form has been spliced to the rootstock. These beeches are an original Henslow planting from the 1840s illustrating variation within species: examples of mutants, (or 'monstrosities', as Henslow would have called them) produced by random and abrupt changes in the genetic code.

19. *Pinus monophylla* (single-leaved nut pine)

This example of the single-leaved nut pine is, at 11.8m, a champion tree that far exceeds many specimens in the wild. Although the roots heaved out of the ground during a storm in 2000, our attractive, pyramidal specimen fortunately came to rest on a lower branch and continues to thrive. Native to the semi-desert in Nevada and California, it obviously enjoys the dry climate of Cambridge. It regularly produces large, viable seeds, known as pinyon nuts.

In winter, seek out *Pinus* × *holfordiana* towering closeby, strung with great banana-like bunches of enormous cones, each a handspan long. There are usually fallen cones on the ground, but be aware, they are incredibly sticky with resin! This hybrid arose at Westonbirt Aboretum (owned and planted by the Holford family) around 1904, a cross between the Mexican white pine, *Pinus ayacahuite*, and the blue pine, *Pinus wallichiana*.

20. *Quercus x warburgii* (Cambridge oak)

A the heart of the Gilbert-Carter Memorial Area stands the Cambridge oak. It appears to have originated, along with a tree growing at the Royal Botanic Gardens, Kew, from the nursery of Messrs Smith of Worcester between 1873 and 1875 from seeds of *Quercus rugosa* sent from Genoa Botanic Garden. It is thought to be a hybrid of *Q. rugosa*, an evergreen species from USA, Mexico and Central America, and the British native, *Q. robur*.

Each May it is a superb sight when the leathery over-wintered leaves are finally shed, the new coppery-red foliage unfurls and the tree is festooned with tasseled bunches of golden-yellow catkins. The common name of 'the Cambridge oak' was coined in recognition of our well-known and magnificent specimen.

21. *Pyrus communis* (wild pear)

This is a fine specimen of the true wild pear tree. Its hollow trunk was filled with bricks and covered in tar in the 1960s following arboricultural practice of the time. The tree is gradually growing around the bricks and encasing them. This treatment for branch-loss is no longer recommended, but it did inspire a recent book, *The Magic Brick Tree*, devised, written and illustrated by young carers in Cambridge, telling of a secret kingdom behind the bricks.

22. *Alnus subcordata* (Caucasian alder)

The Caucasian alder towers over the birch collection, measuring a mighty 17.5m, making it one of our champion trees. The attractive slender male catkins appear exceptionally early, often by mid-December or early January.

In winter, the tree trunks of many of the surrounding birches are a highlight, from the apricot and pink tones of the Chinese red birch, *Betula albosinensis*, to the bright white of the Himalayan birch, *Betula utilis* var. *jacquemontii*.

23. *Fraxinus ornus* (manna ash)

The manna ash makes an attractive, domed tree that in early May is smothered in hay-scented, creamy-white flowers. The flowers have delicate, skinny petals gathered

REMARKABLE

Isaac
NEWTON

Robin Wilson & Raymond Flood

PITKIN

Introduction

The man of science

Why doesn't the moon fall from the sky? Why don't things fall sideways? Why does the tide turn and wash away a sandcastle? Where do the colours in the rainbow come from? A child asks the questions. Isaac Newton gave us the answers.

Newton liked a challenge and refused to be beaten, by a school bully or by a puzzle that nobody else could solve. By the time he was 23, he had found the key to unlock the secrets of the universe. As he said:

If I have seen further it is by standing on the shoulders of Giants.

Newton experimenting with light, from a painting by J.A. Houston.

For this country-bred boy, enjoyment of all things mechanical led him on the road to discovery. When a problem caught his interest, he sought out books to find an answer. This 'needing to know' took Newton in to mathematics, astronomy, mechanics and physics, and even into the workings of the universe itself.

Although not at first an outstanding scholar, Newton later became a professor of mathematics at the University of Cambridge. In the meantime he had lived through civil war in England, Charles I's execution, Cromwell's rule, the Restoration of Charles II, London's Great Plague, and the Great Fire of 1666.

Plague in Cambridge had sent Newton home to Lincolnshire in 1665. Here he had time to think, and in just one year he made world-changing discoveries in gravitation, mathematics and optics.

Laws universal

The young scientist's theory of gravity was his answer to the question of how the universe is held together. His big idea was made known to the outside world in 1687 when Newton published his *Principia Mathematica*, one of the greatest contributions ever made to science. It showed how a few mathematical laws explain the whole universe, linking what happens on earth to what happens beyond.

Insights

Isaac Newton lived in an age of discovery and rapid change. The Royal Society of London was founded in 1660, and in 1671 Newton showed its members his new telescope that used a reflecting mirror instead of lenses – a result of Newton's

Isaac Newton at 60, by Charles Jervas.

research into optics, in which he sought the secrets of light and colour. With his telescope he had seen the moons of the planet Jupiter.

Newton's work brought him public rewards. He became a Member of Parliament and Master of the Royal Mint. He was made President of the Royal Society and a Foreign Associate of the French Academy of Sciences. In 1705 he was knighted by Queen Anne.

Newton's study extended beyond mathematics, physics, astronomy, mechanics, dynamics and optics, into alchemy, chemical experiments, theology and biblical chronology. Whatever took his interest demanded his focused attention.

Isaac Newton had one of the greatest scientific minds of all time. When stimulated by a query or problem, his mathematical genius and power of concentrated thought enabled him to work through to a solution. The laws and principles set out in mathematical form in the *Principia* have guided the development of modern physical science.

Early Years

Woolsthorpe Manor

Woolsthorpe Manor, the birthplace of Isaac Newton in the tiny hamlet of Woolsthorpe in the parish of Colsterworth in Lincolnshire, was a modest stone farmhouse. It had been inherited by his father, an illiterate but prosperous yeoman farmer (also called Isaac), who lived with his wife Hannah. The farm was successful and together they raised over 200 sheep and 40 head of cattle, and grew hay, oats and corn, on his 100 acres of land. Isaac Newton was born on Christmas Day, 1642. Very premature, small and frail, and not expected to survive, he later claimed to have been:

So little they could put him into a quart pot & so weakly that he was forced to have a bolster all round his neck to keep it on his shoulders.

Indeed, two women sent to collect some supplies from a neighbour did not bother to hurry back, doubting that he would still be alive on their return.

Woolsthorpe Manor in Lincolnshire, Newton's childhood home, in a print of 1835.

Isaac's father had died almost three months before the birth of his son, and in 1646, when the small child was barely three years old, Hannah married again and moved to the nearby village of North Witham to live with her new husband, a wealthy elderly clergyman and widower named Barnabas Smith.

Young Isaac was left at Woolsthorpe in the care of his maternal grandmother, a period of his life that he resented for ever after and which surely helped to create the tortured and neurotic personality that he eventually became.

It was an eventful time to be growing up. The Civil War was raging, the Battle of Naseby had taken place in 1645, and the execution of King Charles I occurred when young Isaac was just six years old. But such incidents barely affected the young lad, who attended local schools to learn to read and write and carry out basic arithmetical calculations.

Barnabas Smith and Hannah produced three children, and in 1653, the year when Cromwell was appointed Lord Protector and Isaac was ten years old, his stepfather died and Hannah moved back to Woolsthorpe with her new family.

Woolsthorpe Manor today.

School Life

In 1655, when Isaac Newton was 12, Hannah decided that he should be sent to school in Grantham, seven miles to the north of Woolsthorpe. At that time the Free Grammar School of King Edward VI (now The King's School) consisted mainly of a single schoolroom in which, pursuing the original purpose of such schools, the pupils learned to read, write and speak Latin, together with Bible studies, Greek and arithmetic.

During his time in Grantham, Isaac lodged in the attic of the High Street home of William Clarke, the local apothecary. Here he learned about the composition of medicines and how to mix chemicals, an interest that never left him.

Isaac was also fascinated with making things. He filled the house of the long-suffering Mr Clarke with sundials, and constructed a 4-foot-high water clock. He also

Newton's schoolroom, now the library of The King's School, Grantham.

made kites and paper lanterns illuminated by candles, and even a working model of a windmill, powered by a live mouse which set it in motion by continually reaching out for some corn that had been strategically placed.

A change of attitude

At first Isaac neglected his studies, but the situation changed dramatically one day when another student kicked him hard in the stomach on the way to school. Although light in stature, Isaac challenged him to an after-school fight and with great determination gave him such a beating that the assailant 'declared he would fight no more'.

From that moment Isaac determined to study hard, eventually rising to become head boy of the school.

A poor farmer

When Isaac reached the age of 17, his mother decided that he should return to Woolsthorpe and manage the estate. But Isaac was not cut out for farming. To Hannah's continued frustration he built dams in streams while his sheep strayed into their neighbours' fields (he was once fined for this), and on market days

MAKER OF ALL SORTS

According to Newton's friend and biographer, William Stukeley, Isaac

busyed himself at home, in making knickknacks of divers sorts, & models of wood, of whatever his fancy led him to. For which purpose he furnished himself with little saws, hatchets, hammers, and a whole shop of tools, which he would use with great dexterity, as if he had been brought up to the trade.

in Grantham he let his servant sell the farm's produce and purchase the necessary supplies while he read books and constructed wooden models.

Eventually, seeing that Isaac was wasting his time in farming, Henry Stokes (Isaac's headmaster) and William Ayscough (Hannah's brother and a graduate of Cambridge University) persuaded Hannah that Isaac should return to school and prepare himself for study in Cambridge.

The Free Grammar School of King Edward VI, Grantham.

Cambridge

The Great Court of Trinity College, showing the Chapel and the Great Gate. Newton's room was to the left of the Great Gate on the first floor.

In June 1661 Isaac Newton entered Trinity College, the University of Cambridge's largest college, as an undergraduate. Although his mother was wealthy, she provided him with only limited financial support, and he initially had to work his passage, carrying out such menial tasks as cleaning the Fellows' shoes and waiting on table at mealtimes. These requirements came to an end in April 1664 when he was elected a Scholar of the College.

An independent course

Newton was out of sympathy with the University's curriculum, which demanded the study of traditional Aristotelian philosophy and science. Instead he read books that interested him: geometry from Euclid and from René Descartes, astronomy from Johannes Kepler and Galileo Galilei, philosophy from Thomas Hobbes, and contemporary mathematics from John Wallis of Oxford University. He undoubtedly also received some instruction from Isaac Barrow, the first holder of the newly-created Lucasian Chair of Mathematics.

A notebook showing Newton's expenses during a visit to Cambridge prior to his being admitted as a student. Included here are a Stilton cheese (2s.), a chamber pot (2s.2d.) and 'a table to jot down ye number of my cloathes in the wash' (1s.).

Newton graduated with a BA degree early in 1665, but later in that year his Cambridge career was temporarily interrupted by the Great Plague (see pages 12–13). In the spring of 1667 the University reopened, and Newton returned to Trinity where he was elected a Fellow of the College.

Here he quickly started to climb the academic ladder and within two years, at the age of only 26, he replaced Isaac Barrow as Lucasian Professor of Mathematics. Over the centuries this position has been held by many distinguished Cambridge figures, with Stephen Hawking as a recent occupant. Newton held the Lucasian Chair for 32 years, by which time he had moved to London to take charge of the Royal Mint (see pages 24–25).

MATHEMATICAL BRIDGE

Behind Queens' College is Cambridge's so-called 'Mathematical Bridge'. Built in wood, this footbridge is often claimed to have been designed by Newton so as to require no supporting bolts. It was actually built in 1749 at a cost of about £400.

NEWTON'S STATUE

Louis François Roubiliac's statue of Newton stands in Trinity College Chapel. In Book III of *The Prelude*, 1850, the poet William Wordsworth wrote:

*The antechapel where the statue
    stood
Of Newton with his prism, & silent
    face,
The marble index of a mind for ever
Voyaging through strange seas of
    Thought, alone.*

NEWTON
Qui genus humanum ingenio superavit.

Newton's Contemporaries

The monarchy had been restored in 1660 with the return from the Continent of King Charles II. The new king was interested in science, and with his support and encouragement the Royal Society was soon established. Formed to promote experimental science, 'The Royal Society of London for Improving Natural Knowledge' received its Royal Charter in 1662.

In 1675 Charles II also founded the Royal Observatory at Greenwich to improve the accuracy of the tables describing the moon's motion, in order to enable ships at sea to determine their longitude by using the position of the moon against the fixed stars.

The diarist John Evelyn described Charles II as:

a prince of many virtues and many great imperfections, debonair, easy of access, not bloody or cruel . . . he had a laboratory, and knew of many empirical medicines, and the easier mechanical mathematics. He loved planting and building, and brought in a politer way of living, which passed to luxury and intolerable expense.

Robert Hooke's *Micrographia* of 1665 was the first work to present images seen under a microscope. Here we see his drawing of a flea.

This engraved frontispiece of an early history of the Royal Society, captures the spirit of Restoration science. Charles II is crowned with a laurel wreath, while the books and scientific instruments indicate the practical and experimental interests of the Society's members.

The Royal Observatory, built by Christopher Wren, cost within 5 per cent of its original budget of £500.

SOCIETY OF SCIENTISTS

Robert Boyle, Christopher Wren, Robert Hooke and Edmond Halley all played significant roles in the scientific life of late 17th-century England, and all contributed to the early history of the Royal Society:

- Boyle made many pioneering contributions to science and was particularly interested in chemical phenomena. He also found the relationship between the volume and pressure of a gas which is now known as 'Boyle's Law'.

- Although now mainly remembered as an architect, Wren's early career was as an astronomer. Isaac Newton ranked him as one of the outstanding geometers of his age.

- For over 35 years Hooke held the position of Professor of Geometry at Gresham College, London, where the Royal Society held its meetings. As the Society's Curator of Experiments he was required to design and present experiments there on a regular basis.

- Without the support and encouragement of Halley (of 'Halley's comet' fame) Newton's greatest work, the *Principia Mathematica*, would never have appeared (see pages 16–17).

Plague and Fire

In the summer of 1665 the dreaded bubonic plague reached Cambridge, and the University closed and sent the students away. Newton returned to Lincolnshire and continued his investigations into mathematics, gravity and optics, and in a relatively short period of time laid the foundations for his ground-breaking work on these subjects. Fifty years later he recalled the plague years of 1665–66, working in the rural peace and calm of Lincolnshire:

In those days I was in the prime of my age for invention & minded Mathematics & Philosophy more than at any time since.

TERROR AND DEATH

In this engraving, *Scenes from the Great Plague of 1665*, people in London flee from St Paul's and bury the dead in Covent Garden. Below the illustration appear the following words:

For he that durst (in the dead hours of gloomy midnight) have been so valiant ast to have walkt through the still and melancholy streets. What thinke you should have bene his musicke? Surely the loude grones of raving sicke men, the struggling panges of soules departing – Servants crying out for maisters: wives for husbands: parents for children, children for their mothers. Here he should have met same frantically running to knock up Sextons: there others fearfully sweating with Coffins to steal dead bodies.

In September 1666, while Newton was still in Lincolnshire making his momentous discoveries, the Great Fire of London destroyed much of the capital city. Although some people thought that the fire put an end to the epidemic, it is now believed that the plague was already well past its peak before the fire took place.

THE KEY TO DISCOVERY

Newton's discoveries during this time, while he was still only in his early 20s, would make him one of the leading mathematicians and scientists in the world. How was he able to do it? One reason, suggested by the distinguished economist John Maynard Keynes, was

. . . that the clue to his mind is to be found in his unusual powers of continuous concentrated introspection. . . . Newton could hold a problem in his mind for hours and days and weeks until it surrendered to him its secret.

A 17th-century engraving of the Great Fire of London.

Newton and the Apple

One of the most celebrated stories in scientific folklore is a tale that Newton recalled in old age. Seeing an apple fall, he realised that the gravitational force that pulls the apple to earth is the same as the force that keeps the moon orbiting around the earth, and the earth orbiting around the sun.

Before Newton

In 1543 Nicolaus Copernicus had transformed astronomy by replacing the ancient Greek earth-centred system of planetary motion by a heliocentric model with the sun at the centre and the earth as just one of several planets travelling in circular orbits around it.

Almost a century later, Galileo Galilei compared the two planetary systems, coming out strongly in favour of the Copernican one: this led to his trial and house arrest by the Inquisition which forced him to recant his Copernican views.

Galileo also determined how position, velocity and acceleration of a moving body vary with time, laying the mathematical foundations that underpinned his belief that the earth really moves. Its mathematical form led to further advances by others, and particularly by Isaac Newton who was born in the year that Galileo died.

Nicolaus Copernicus (above) and Galileo Galilei (left).

An artist's impression of Newton and his famous apple.

Copernicus's heliocentric system, which placed the sun (not the earth) at the centre of the solar system.

SYSTEM OF THE WORLD

In his thought experiment from *A Treatise of the System of the World* of 1728, Newton imagined projecting an object horizontally from a mountain labelled V (see illustration below).

As the speed of projection increases, the object lands further and further away at the points on the earth labelled D, E, F and G.

Eventually, if the speed is great enough, it continues to circle the earth in much the same way as the moon stays in orbit.

WHY THE PLANETS ORBIT

Planetary motion is governed by a universal law of gravitation, *the inverse square law*:

The force of attraction between two objects varies as the product of their masses, and inversely as the square of the distance between them.

For example, doubling each mass increases the force between them by a factor of 4, and increasing the distance between them tenfold decreases the force by a factor of 100.

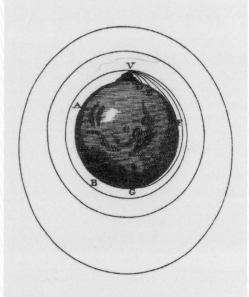

Gravity and the *Principia*

The year 1687 saw the publication of *Newton's Mathematical Principles of Natural Philosophy*, known as the *Principia*. In this book, possibly the greatest scientific book of all time, Newton unified terrestrial and celestial mechanics for the first time, investigating the motion of bodies both on earth and in the heavens, and accounting for the orbits of comets, the variation of the tides, the flattening of the earth at its poles due to the earth's rotation, and the movement of objects in a resisting medium.

His approach used ideas from geometry, with forces, velocities, accelerations, distances and times all represented by lines and areas.

NEWTON'S LAWS OF MOTION

Newton opened the *Principia* with three laws of motion:

- Every body continues in its state of rest, or of uniform motion in a straight line, unless it is compelled to change that state by forces impressed on it.
- Any change of motion is proportional to the force, and is made in the direction of the line in which the force is applied.
- To any action there is an equal and opposite reaction.

'Newton's cradle' (below) is based on his laws of motion. When an end-ball is raised and then released it strikes the next one, but instead of all the remaining balls moving, only the one at the further end does. The force of collision is transmitted through the intervening balls.

PHILOSOPHIÆ

NATURALIS

PRINCIPIA

MATHEMATICA.

Autore *JS. NEWTON*, *Trin. Coll. Cantab. Soc.* Matheseos Professore *Lucasiano*, & Societatis Regalis Sodali.

IMPRIMATUR·

S. PEPYS, *Reg. Soc.* PRÆSES.

Julii 5. 1686.

LONDINI,

Jussu Societatis Regiæ ac Typis *Josephi Streater*. Prostat apud plures Bibliopolas. *Anno* MDCLXXXVII.

The first edition of the *Principia*, published in 1687.

In 1609 the German mathematician and astronomer Johannes Kepler proposed that

Planets travel around the sun in elliptical orbits

and that

The line from the sun to a planet sweeps out equal areas in equal periods of time

It follows that the planet moves most quickly when it is near to the sun.

Kepler had derived these laws from observed results, and many years later, in the *Principia*, Newton explained why they are true, based on his laws of motion and his universal law of gravitation, the inverse square law.

A diagram illustrating Kepler's laws of planetary motion.

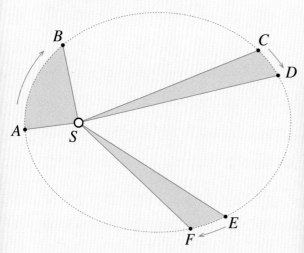

Halley's comet in 1682: it last visited in 1986 and will return in 2061.

HALLEY'S COMET

It was Edmond Halley who coaxed and cajoled Newton into publishing the *Principia* and who paid for its publication. Using Newton's laws, Halley attempted to fit observations of recent comets to elliptical orbits, suggesting that the comet of 1682 might be the same as those that had been observed on previous occasions. Halley's comet became his memorial when it duly returned in 1758–59.

Halley's prediction of the comet's return was one of the most successful vindications of Newtonian theory, demonstrating its power to explain hitherto mysterious phenomena, and showing them to be predictable and subject to the same laws as the sun, moon and planets.

Optics

We do not know for certain how Newton's interest in light started: we know that while an undergraduate he had bought a prism at a fair, or maybe it was the stimulus of Robert Hooke's *Micrographia* (see page 10) that started him thinking about how colours are produced and what their relationship is to white light. Newton and Hooke later had a bitter disagreement about the nature of light and colours.

The colours of light

Newton's investigations led him to conclude that white light was not something that gave rise to colours when 'modified', but rather that it was composed of different colours that could not be changed further. This formed the basis of his new theory of light and colour.

Newton's drawing of his 'crucial experiment'. In this he showed that when light from the sun is refracted through a prism and then one colour is refracted through a second prism, it undergoes no further change.

Why do we say that there are just seven colours in a rainbow? Newton attempted to link his ideas on light and sound by exhibiting a correspondence between the colours in the spectrum with the seven notes, A–G, of the musical scale.

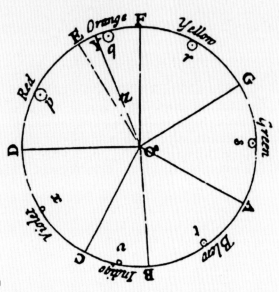

Newton's telescope

Newton's first optical contribution to become widely known was not his investigation into the nature of colours, but his reflecting telescope. This instrument, only 6 inches long, used mirrors instead of lenses to reflect the light to form an image, and avoided the problem of colouring around the edges in a refracting telescope whose lenses refract different colours by different amounts.

Newton's telescope caused a sensation and ensured his election to the Royal Society. He had great manual skills: he designed and built the telescope himself, also making the tools he required. Newton eventually published his optical researches in his 1704 book *Opticks* (see page 25), which was viewed by many as a model of how to do experimental science.

Replica of Newton's reflecting telescope.

NEWTON'S RINGS

Another important phenomenon that Newton investigated was the appearance of coloured concentric rings that occur when two pieces of glass (one flat and one convex) are in contact. This pattern is now known as *Newton's rings*.

Mathematics

The 17th century witnessed the beginnings of modern mathematics. Fundamental problems, such as that of determining the orbits of the heavenly bodies, were solved or investigated with novel techniques, while new areas of the subject came into being, such as coordinate geometry and calculus.

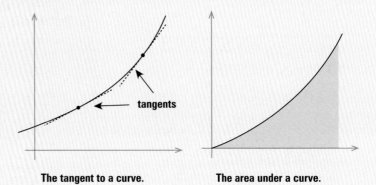

The tangent to a curve.

The area under a curve.

Calculus

Calculus is made up from two seemingly unrelated strands, now called *differentiation* and *integration*. Differentiation is concerned with how fast things move or change, and is used in the finding of velocities and tangents to curves. Integration is used to find areas of shapes in two-dimensional space or volumes in three dimensions.

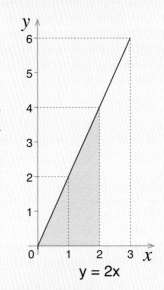

Differentiate to find tangents.

Integrate to find areas.

$y = x^2$

$y = 2x$

An example showing the inverse processes of differentiation and integration.

As the 17th century progressed it was gradually realised that these two strands are intimately related. As both Newton and Gottfried Leibniz explained, they are inverse processes – if we follow either by the other, we return to our starting point.

The philosopher Gottfried Wilhelm Leibniz.

Newton and Leibniz

Newton and Leibniz had different motivations: Leibniz was concerned with tangents and curves while Newton focused on motion – how things change with time, or 'flow'. His tangent problems involved velocities, and in his treatise on fluxions (flowing quantities), he presented rules for calculating these velocities.

The frontispiece of Newton's *Method of Fluxions*, linking ancient Greek mathematicians (left) with traditional 17th-century sporting pursuits.

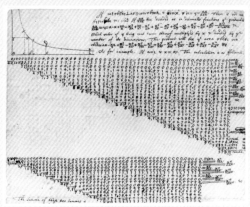

This manuscript shows part of Newton's calculation of the area under a hyperbola. His working, where he adds terms of an infinite series, extends to 55 decimal places. Newton's realisation of the importance of such series was a major contribution to mathematics.

NEWTON'S CURVES

Newton was interested in the properties of curves. The Greeks had studied the 'quadratic curves' that are obtained by slicing a cone in different ways: an ellipse (of which the circle is a special case), a parabola and a hyperbola. Newton looked at the corresponding problem of classifying 'cubic curves', discovered that there are 78 different types, and published 72 of them in his *Opticks*. This achievement was far ahead of its time.

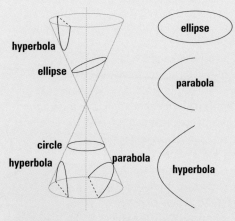

The conic sections: an ellipse, a parabola and a hyperbola.

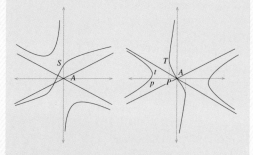

Two of Newton's 'cubic curves'.

Alchemy

Although Isaac Newton is remembered mainly for his work in mathematics and physics, he spent thousands of hours over several decades on alchemy and divinity – subjects with which he became better acquainted than almost anyone else. Because of his unconventional views, he felt the need to keep his extensive writings on these subjects, amounting to over a million words, largely secret. For many years afterwards these preoccupations were dismissed as of little value, but recent scholars have come to view them more as connecting with other aspects of his work.

Changing materials

Newton's interest in alchemy can be traced back to his schoolboy days in Grantham when William Clarke, the local apothecary, introduced him to the mixing of chemicals. In the 17th century, alchemy was that part of 'chymistry' which attempted to mimic the transmutations in nature (such as the change from a tadpole to a frog) in order to convert one substance to another – and in particular, from ordinary metals (such as lead) to silver and gold. The subject was intimately tied up with the occult and involved experiments with substances such as mercury that combined well with other metals.

For his extensive alchemical experiments throughout the 1670s and

1680s Newton designed and built furnaces and other equipment, and every spring and autumn he hid himself away in his laboratory for up to six weeks of frenzied activity, frequently forgetting to eat or sleep.

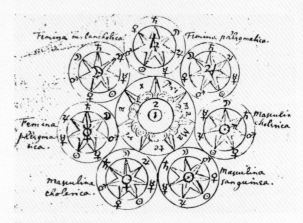

Newton's drawing of the philosopher's stone, which was supposedly involved in the process of turning base metals into gold.

Newton's alchemical laboratory at Trinity College was on the right beyond the trees, next to the chapel.

Divinity

Newton's views on religion were highly controversial. Although believing in a Supreme God he described as 'eternal, infinite, and absolutely perfect', he refused to countenance the Christian doctrine of the Trinity of the Father, Son and the Holy Spirit as one and the same.

Newton knew the ancient texts as well as any theologian in the kingdom, having compared them assiduously in their original languages of Latin, Greek and Hebrew. Starting from these original writings he spent much time in trying to date the Creation and, using verses from the Biblical book of Ezekiel, he managed to reconstruct the layout of Solomon's temple in Jerusalem.

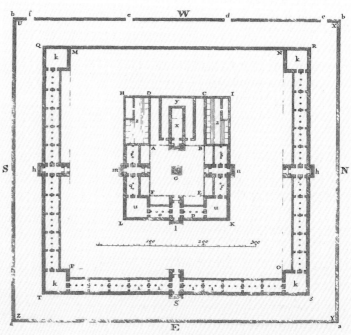

Newton's reconstruction of the Temple of Solomon.

Using discretion

Newton kept his anti-Trinitarian views to himself, as they would have been considered as heretical by both the Church of England and the University of Cambridge. However, the statutes of his Lucasian Chair of Mathematics required him to take holy orders after seven years and Newton, unwilling to do so, was expecting to have to resign his professorship. At the last moment Isaac Barrow, his predecessor in the Lucasian Chair, managed to obtain a special dispensation from King Charles II releasing Newton from this obligation.

The first of twelve editions of Newton's study of Biblical prophecy, as presented in the Book of Daniel and the Revelation of St John.

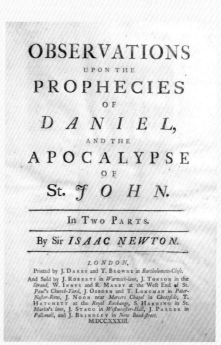

OBSERVATIONS
UPON THE
PROPHECIES
OF
DANIEL,
AND THE
APOCALYPSE
OF
St. JOHN.

In Two Parts.

By Sir ISAAC NEWTON.

LONDON,
Printed by J. Darby and T. Browne in Bartholomew-Close.
And Sold by J. Roberts in Warwick-lane, J. Tonson in the Strand, W. Innys and R. Manby at the West End of St. Paul's Church-Yard, J. Osborn and T. Longman in Pater-Noster-Row, J. Noon near Mercers Chapel in Cheapside, T. Hatchett at the Royal Exchange, S. Harding in St. Martin's lane, J. Stagg in Westminster-Hall, J. Parker in Pall-mall, and J. Brindley in New Bond-street.
M.DCC.XXXIII.

London

In 1696 Isaac Newton, then in his early 50s, left Cambridge to become Warden of the Royal Mint in London. For the last 30 years of his life the secretive and retiring scholar became an influential public figure, gaining power and position which he then ruthlessly employed to achieve his aims.

Public life

Newton was an extremely efficient administrator and a calculating political operator, and he immediately set to sorting out the problems at the Mint. Because he could do nothing in a half-hearted way, he took charge of the recoinage that was needed to resolve a monetary crisis in the economy. But his duties went beyond administration as he was responsible for prosecuting counterfeiters and recommending their execution when he thought this appropriate, a task that he undertook with the same intensity and commitment that he used for his academic researches. Newton was successful in reducing the amount of counterfeiting, and in 1699 became Master of the Mint.

QUEEN ANNE'S
CORONATION MEDAL

Among Newton's activities at the Royal Mint was the design of commemorative medals. One of these medals celebrated the Coronation of Queen Anne in 1702, and depicts Anne as the goddess Athena striking down a two-headed monster representing the threat of Catholic rivals to her throne.

A coining screw press in operation. The person at the centre inserted the blanks and removed them after they were struck by the press: this happened 20–30 times per minute as the balance arm was swung back and forth.

In this Victorian reconstruction of a Royal Society meeting, Newton is seated in the centre behind a table on which is laid the Society's mace.

During his early years in London, Newton paid very little attention to the Royal Society, which was in a poor state both financially and in the contributions of its Fellows to its activities. But after the death in March 1703 of Robert Hooke, with whom Newton had had bitter disputes on gravity and light (see pages 18–19), he re-engaged with the Society and in November of that year was elected its President, a position that he held until his death. As with the Mint, Newton applied his formidable powers and organisational skills to restoring the Society's fortunes.

Opticks

Newton's appointment as President seems to have rekindled his interest in science, and in the following year he brought out his *Opticks*, his work on light which, although mainly written long before, was probably delayed by his disputes with Hooke. Written in English, rather than Latin, *Opticks* was easier to understand than the *Principia*, and it became a popular book that was accessible to a wide audience.

Recognition

Newton's success and public recognition were increasing, and in 1705 he was knighted by Queen Anne for services to the State. He was the first British scientist to receive this honour.

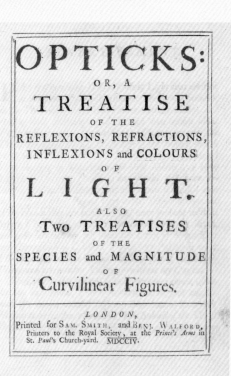

OPTICKS:

OR, A

TREATISE

OF THE

REFLEXIONS, REFRACTIONS, INFLEXIONS and COLOURS

OF

LIGHT.

ALSO

Two **TREATISES**

OF THE

SPECIES and MAGNITUDE

OF

Curvilinear Figures.

LONDON,

Printed for SAM. SMITH, and BENJ. WALFORD, Printers to the Royal Society, at the *Prince's Arms* in St. *Paul's* Church-yard. MDCCIV.

The title page of *Opticks*, Newton's 1704 book on light.

Final Years

Although his health was failing in his final years, Isaac Newton continued working to ensure that Newtonian philosophy would spread and become established. He supported the appointment of his followers to university positions where they could lecture and write textbooks that supported his approach.

One thing that continued to feature was his capacity to take offence and become involved in arguments, such as a major disagreement with John Flamsteed, the first Astronomer Royal, over access to the latter's astronomical observations, and with Leibniz over the invention of calculus, with Newton's followers accusing Leibniz of plagiarism. Newton arranged for a supposedly 'independent' commission to investigate the issue, which unsurprisingly ruled in his favour.

Isaac Newton died in his 85th year on 20 March 1727 and his body lay in state in Westminster Abbey for the week before his funeral. At the funeral service his coffin was carried by two dukes, three earls and the Lord Chancellor. The French writer Voltaire observed that:

> He was buried like a king who had done well by his subjects.

A portrait by James Thornhill of Isaac Newton in his late 60s.

A death mask was used in creating Newton's features on his tomb at Westminster Abbey.

NEWTON'S MONUMENT

The tomb of Isaac Newton in Westminster Abbey was erected in 1731, and its rich symbolism refers to the many areas of Newton's work.

The boys on the front of the sarcophagus play with a prism, the reflecting telescope, a furnace and newly minted coins, while one boy weighs the sun and the planets.

Above the sarcophagus reclines the figure of Newton, his right elbow resting on several books that represent his great works. His left hand points to a scroll, held by two cherubs, picturing the solar system and a mathematical series.

Above Newton, a celestial globe shows the signs of the Zodiac, the great comet of 1680–81 and the solstice position by which Newton dated the ancient Greek expedition of the Argonauts. On top of the globe sits the figure of Astronomy.

If you visit the tomb you will find the exhortation:

Let Mortals rejoice that there has existed such and so great an ornament of the human race.

This shows the extent of his standing and the view of his achievements among his contemporaries. In the nearly 300 years since then, Newton's reputation has hardly faded and he is still considered by many as the greatest scientific mind of all time.

Newton's Legacy

Nature and Nature's laws lay hid in night:
God said 'Let Newton be!' and all was light.

Alexander Pope intended his lines for Newton's memorial in Westminster Abbey. They show what the world thought of the famous scientist in 1730, and for the next 200 and more years. Newton's principles guided later scientists, even as their discoveries began to challenge his 17th-century ideas. For fellow-scientists his place is still at the top of the tree. To others, his name invokes the flash of inspiration (sparked perhaps by a falling apple) that may have given the key to understanding the universe.

Optics

Newton's research founded the science of colour (as used, for example, in spectrum analysis). By 1675 he had developed a theory of light to account for reflection, refraction, colour and diffraction. Today's most powerful terrestrial optical telescopes are modern versions of his reflecting telescope. The Hubble space telescope was also designed with mirrors, to deliver the clearer image which was Newton's aim.

Mathematics and motion

Newton's calculus produced a tool for working out difficult mathematical problems. It has been called the most important single mathematical invention since the time of the ancient Greeks. His three laws of motion form the basis of modern physics, and contributed to many advances during the Industrial Revolution. Using his laws, Newton predicted that the earth is not perfectly round, and discovered how the gravitational pull of the sun and moon create the ocean's tides.

FAME ABROAD

Newton's *Principia* was an instant success in England. The antiquary and biographer John Aubrey enthused about 'the greatest Discovery in Nature that ever was since the World's Creation'. There was immediate enthusiasm for the *Principia* in Italy and the Netherlands, rather less in France where Newton's ideas on gravitation contradicted those of René Descartes. The first French translation of the *Principia* was by Emilie, Marquise du Châtelet, who added a perceptive commentary, and with her lover, Voltaire, did much to spread Newton's ideas in France.

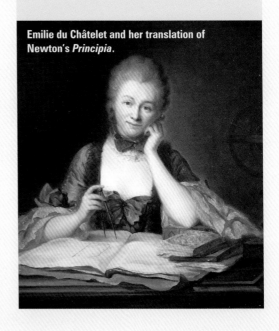

Emilie du Châtelet and her translation of Newton's *Principia*.

An allegorical monument to Sir Isaac Newton was painted by Giovanni Battista Pittoni and Domenico and Giuseppe Valeriani shortly after Newton's death in 1727. It contains many images related to Newton's work, including a version of his prism experiment with light emerging from above the urn that contains Newton's remains.

The rational view

At Cambridge, which still taught Aristotle's ideas, Newton studied for himself the works of more recent thinkers, including René Descartes. In a student notebook he wrote, 'Plato is my friend, Aristotle is my friend, but my best friend is truth'. His search for truths to explain the world around him led Newton to think of a universe based on natural laws that could be understood by reason. The idea was a seed of the 18th-century Enlightenment, when Voltaire and Locke applied it to politics, and Adam Smith to economics.

A new theory

In 1905 Albert Einstein produced his special theory of relativity – a new way of thinking about space and time that challenged those of Newton. Yet Einstein declared that without Newton his work would have been impossible, and kept Newton's picture on his study wall. Newtonian physics still explains many of the phenomena we observe in the world and is used to determine the paths and orbits of our spacecraft and satellites.

It can be argued that every physicist following Newton through to the present day owes him a debt: James Clerk Maxwell and Heinrich Hertz on electromagnetic radiation, Max Planck on quantum theory, Niels Bohr on atomic structure, and Stephen Hawking on cosmology. They, and many others, have felt the power of Newton's influence.

Newton's statue in Grantham.

In 1927, on the 200th anniversary of Newton's death, Einstein described him as a 'shining spirit' who 'deserves our deepest veneration'.

NEWTON IN ART

Newton was painted in his lifetime by many artists, including Godfrey Kneller, Charles Jervas and James Thornhill. His image has also appeared in works by painters, sculptors and engravers, and his character has featured in films, plays and stories, where he stands as a representation of science or intellect.

The famous 1795 image of *Newton: Personification of Man Limited by Reason* by the visionary poet-artist William Blake depicts the scientist, naked on a rock below the sea, measuring a geometrical diagram with compasses. Blake was opposed to many of Newton's views.

Blake's image is echoed in the 12-foot-high bronze that stands outside the British Library in London. Eduardo Paolozzi's work of 1995 shows Newton measuring the universe, under mathematical law. His body resembles a mechanical object.

Fittingly, as Master of the Mint, Newton has also been depicted on coins and banknotes, including the last £1 note issued by the Bank of England, and on many postage stamps from around the world.

The surrealist Salvador Dali cast a number of bronzes of Newton, ranging from miniatures to public sculptures. *Homage to Newton* shows an open torso of Newton holding a suspended ball or apple.

18P

PHILOSOPHIÆ
NATURALIS
PRINCIPIA
MATHEMATICA

Sir ISAAC NEWTON (1642-1727)

One of four British stamps issued in 1987 to commemorate the 300th anniversary of the publication of Newton's *Principia*.

Around the edge of many of Britain's £2 coins appear the words 'STANDING ON THE SHOULDERS OF GIANTS'.

Newton, after William Blake, by Eduardo Paolozzi.

Places to Visit

Lincolnshire

Woolsthorpe Manor (National Trust)
Water Lane, Woolsthorpe by Colsterworth
near Grantham, Lincolnshire NG33 5PD, UK
Tel: 01476 862823 / (+44) 1476 862823
www.nationaltrust.org.uk/woolsthorpe-manor

Grantham

Grantham Museum
St Peter's Hill, Grantham,
Lincolnshire NG31 6PY, UK
Tel: 01476 568783 / (+44) 1476 568783
www.granthammuseum.org.uk

Sir Isaac Newton statue
St Peter's Hill, Grantham

The King's School
Brook Street, Grantham,
Lincolnshire NG31 6RP, UK
Visits by personal arrangement only:
Tel: 01476 563180 / (+44) 1476 563180
www.kings.lincs.sch.uk

Cambridge

Trinity College
Cambridge CB2 1TQ, UK
Tel: 01223 338400 / (+44) 1223 338400
www.trin.cam.ac.uk

Mathematical Bridge
Queens' College,
Cambridge CB3 9ET, UK
www.queens.cam.ac.uk

London

Westminster Abbey
20 Dean's Yard, Westminster,
London SW1P 3PA, UK
Tel: 020 7222 5152 / (+44) 20 7222 5152
www.westminster-abbey.org

The Royal Society
6–9 Carlton House Terrace
London SW1Y 5AG, UK
Tel: 020 7451 2500 / (+44) 20 7451 2500
www.royalsociety.org

Science Museum
Exhibition Road
South Kensington,
London SW7 2DD, UK
Tel: 020 7942 4000 / (+44) 20 7942 4000
www.sciencemuseum.org.uk

British Library
96 Euston Road,
London NW1 2DB, UK
Tel: 01937 546060 / (+44) 1937 546060
www.bl.uk

Royal Observatory
Blackheath Avenue,
Greenwich,
London SE10 8XJ
Tel: 0 20 8312 6608 / (+44) 20 8312 6608
www.rmg.co.uk

The kitchen of Woolsthorpe Manor, Newton's childhood home.